FANFAN

FANFAN

Alexandre Jardin

Translated from the French by Charles Penwarden

St. Martin's Press
New York

Library of Congress Cataloging-in-Publication Data

Jardin, Alexandre.
[Fanfan. English]
Fanfan / Alexandre Jardin.
p.   cm.
ISBN 0-312-10981-4
1. Man-woman relationships—France—Fiction.   I. Title.
PQ2670.A68F3613   1994
843'.914—dc20   94-2829   CIP

First published in France by Flammarion, 1990.
First published in Great Britain by Abacus, 1993.

First U.S. Edition: July 1994
10 9 8 7 6 5 4 3 2 1

FANFAN

ONE

EVER SINCE I GREW OLD ENOUGH TO LOVE, I HAVE dreamt of wooing a woman without ever giving in to my senses. I have yearned to meet a virtuous young girl who would both adore me and yet still oblige me to contain my passion. Unfortunately, the art of bridling desire is one your twentieth-century woman has forgotten. As an adolescent I had to hold the reins for myself.

I steered clear of the easy lay. I did my best to distil the ferment of love in girls' hearts, leading them step by small step to passion. All my ingenuity was spent in the art of skilful courtship.

Gradually, it became second nature to defer my amatory outpourings. At sixteen, the most I could manage was to muzzle my lust for a few weeks; when I was ready to yield I simply withdrew. But in my eighteenth year I found myself resisting the urgings of my loins for almost six months. I was in a rapture of platonic love. I feasted on angelic thoughts. The more a woman appealed to my imagination, the harder I tried to lock out my libido. To seduce but not succumb, that was my religion, my chosen sport, the axiom of my existence.

Restraining my urges like this made me so ecstatic that it seemed as if only incompleteness could satisfy me – a state of hope-filled frustration. I dreamt of an asymptotic relationship, with my lover and I set on ever-closer trajectories yet never being carried into the same bed. That would be my path to perpetual passion.

The oddness of my conduct and aspirations, which is now apparent to me, will seem less surprising when I tell you about the man my family descends from. This character, with his extraordinary destiny, has inspired three centuries of strange behaviour in those who have inherited his name.

Allow me to introduce myself: Alexandre Crusoé.

Robinson is my ancestor. The novel drawn from his adventures does not relate that before he was washed up on the island, he had, by his young wife Mary, a son who answered to the name of William Crusoé. William is the founder of our line, which became French in the nineteenth century. This information was carefully recorded in our family annals, along with many anecdotes about Robinson which have never been revealed to the public and are stored away in the archives belonging to one of my great-uncles (Frédéric Crusoé).

It was because of this name that I went through school as an outcast. I was constantly being jibed at by my classmates: they couldn't bring themselves to admit that my ancestry could be so fabulous. Yet their mockery only rekindled my pride at having a few drops of Robinson Crusoé's blood in my veins. Now I felt different, destined for a maverick existence.

All the Crusoés have heard this inner voice at one time or another. I know that as young men both my father, Pascal Crusoé, and my grandfather, Jean Crusoé, felt the need to live on a giant scale – and well off the beaten track. My brothers too intend to go beyond the limits.

Most of my friends envied my childhood. And they were all mad about our weekends at Verdelot. This was an old priory some hundred kilometres from Paris, which we had named after the local village. My parents used to meet there on Saturdays and Sundays, after a week of voluntary separation. They came with numerous 'friends' and 'girlfriends' who, as the years passed, formed a strange family. Many were famous, nearly all would become so. There, in his workshop, my father made extravagantly useless objects. The adults told fascinating stories, built weird furniture, played poker and cooked together. The men worshipped my mother, who was indeed exorbitantly beautiful, and, so I guessed, fought amongst themselves for the monopoly of her affection. I suspected it was for her that they wrote novels, that some died and others made films, stole or dissipated fortunes – and I am not exaggerating – but I was careful not to dwell on my suspicions. It was enough for me to enjoy the amusing flurry of competition between these men of quality.

My father also had everyone under his spell. He conducted his existence as if every minute were the last, and transformed every weekend into a festival. Often,

3

he would wake us up, my friends and I, in the middle of the night, to get us involved in one of his telephone pranks. His favourite victim was the Minister of the Interior, whom we called regularly on his private line at three in the morning, passing ourselves off as his grand-mother. My mates were most amused. Then, pretending to be worried, Dad would barricade the house to protect us against possible reprisals from the forces of order. We would load cartridges into an old Winchester and fire a few shots out of the window, just to let our imaginary assailants know we were armed. At which point my mother would come out, scold my father and pack us off to bed. Those were the days.

Sometimes, a friend would say:

'Tell me ... what's going on at your place? Who's Pierre?'

'Pierre's Pierre,' I answered.

'And Jacques?'

'Jacques's Jacques.'

'Ah ...'

But I wasn't asking questions. Instead, I nurtured the satisfying thought that the company at Verdelot was great. After all, didn't my friends greatly prefer to spend their weekends with my 'weird family' than in the doldrums of their homes?

I was thirteen when, in the space of ten seconds, my point of view was turned on its head. I had prepared breakfast, tracing 'Happy Mothers' Day' with great application in Chantilly cream on a cake I had baked myself. I made towards my mother's bedroom with the tray, ready to surprise her. Discreetly, I opened the door and was about to let out a joyous 'Happy Mothers'

4

Day, Mum!' when I noticed there was a man on top of her. He was not my father and he had not fallen into the bed by mistake.

Now I could see the other side of Verdelot. Suddenly I had all the answers and no need of the questions. Ever since that morning, I have held my sexuality to be the enemy of my serenity. I have returned to Verdelot only when forced to do so.

My disaffection with the place was completed by my father's subsequent remarks about his work. Since he was incapable of doing anything boring, he had become a novelist and scriptwriter and claimed to nourish his writings with the intense sensations procured by his own extravagant adventures. His mistresses were the women he invited to Verdelot. What were he and my mother playing at? I would rather not know. I have no doubt that his was an excellent method for stimulating the imagination, but such depraved behaviour frightened me; and my fear took on a morbid colouring when I was fifteen. That was the year when a cancer almost landed him in the cemetery. What I took to be licentiousness now struck me as synonymous with mortal risk. I had the obscure feeling that his illness and his vice were somehow connected.

And so from puberty onwards I strove to protect myself from my instincts, by learning to lavish what I hoped would be an endless courtship on the girls I loved. The vehemence of my animal cravings filled me with anxiety: I hungered for the whole fruit, and had a tough time controlling my appetite. But I was also highly partial to those thrilling sensations that torment the sensibility when you hesitate to yield to feeling, when

5

you fear rejection. In love, I felt free from our everyday insignificance.

Most of the girls I courted soon wearied of my restraint. Some had doubts about my heterosexuality. Others supposed I was impotent. Like me, they had no inkling of what caused the secret anxiety that gripped me whenever it was time for decisive action.

Unfortunately, though, my senses were those of my age and my sex, and so I sometimes submitted to their demands. These concessions filled me with panic. Terrified at the thought that my parents' inconstancy might have sent out new shoots within me too, I invariably told my sixteen- or seventeen-year-old lovers that I wanted them to be my Mrs Crusoé, that we would soon have children, and that I would lock them up in a dwelling surrounded by palisades. Equally invariably, and at an incredible speed, they made a run for it.

However, when I was nineteen and at Sciences-Po, I met this student. She wore a grey skirt and jacket and had a hankering for commitment. Eventually, after a few months of methodical courtship – time enough to build up a few memories – I took the decisive step: I kissed Laure de Chantebise and resolved to bury myself in our love for as long as I lived. It was a prospect that fully satisfied her young-woman's aspirations.

I had gone to Sciences-Po after facing a long dilemma between that reassuring avenue and another more risky one: the theatre. I dreamed of writing plays and becoming an actor. But I was apprehensive about throwing myself into an artistic adventure: everyone at Verdelot wrote, directed or acted. Besides, I was tempted by politics too, and at Sciences-Po I vaguely hoped to discover a serious-minded and charming girl who would rescue me from my old milieu.

Laure de Chantebise fulfilled my expectations. She was one small branch on a family tree copiously endowed with brothers, sisters, cousins and other buds. In her world, divorce was not the logical sequel to marriage. When he swore fidelity to the church, your Chantebise meant it. Nor did his clan so much as smile when there was talk of certain eternal values.

Laure was a vivacious young woman with reassuringly simple desires: she wanted a beautiful house and a big family – quite unlike the one at Verdelot. When she spoke, the notion of quiet happiness seemed full of charm. Every day she showed me that a certain conformism has its comforts and that an ordinary and regular existence can bring perfect contentment. With her I discovered that happy people have a history made up of exquisite instants and pleasant evenings. I was captivated by her charms and her bearing, which bespoke a young woman accustomed to classical dance classes. And then I loved her fresh nature and contagious laughter. Only one thing really saddened me: she hated it when I took off my mask, that of the serious and stable young man. My manifestations of sincerity worried her. We talked about everything, except our emotions.

Yet I was sure that with her I would escape the syndrome bequeathed by my parents. Her belief in monogamous bliss would help me strengthen my own and keep me on the straight and narrow. To clinch my new persona, I became an apostle of fidelity. We moved into a studio in Paris next to my mother's and made plans to enter into legal bonds the following summer.

Naturally, my father mocked this taste for everlasting emotions. He kept giving me taunting looks and telling me that, as his son, I could never disown the genes he had passed on to me. When all this became too much, I shouted back that he was just a has-been, that now I had diverted all our family sap into my own veins – all the heritage of Robinson Crusoé.

My mother was less blunt, but her comments were eloquent enough. From time to time, when speaking to Laure she would preface the main sentence with sub-ordinate clauses such as 'if Alexandre leaves you', or 'if one day you should be unfaithful to Alexandre', only adding the 'if' so as not to shock me, but saying it without a trace of conditionality. She wished me well, of course, but she could never imagine a passion capable of being sustained for a whole lifetime.

I could.

I wanted desperately to believe that the heart's move-ments are eternal, that love will triumph over the assaults of the years. Within me there existed a young man for whom the only feelings worth experiencing were imperishable ones, a young man who abhorred the mores of his parents.

That is why at the age of nineteen I had sworn to love only one woman. That was when Laure won me over. She would be my wife, until death do us part; my instincts could go to the devil.

TWO

IN THOSE DAYS I WAS A REGULAR VISITOR TO A LITTLE hotel on the Normandy coast run by my mentor, Monsieur Ti, a most unusual old man.

Though Monsieur Ti had no children to inherit his bat's ears, he hoped to prolong his existence in the mind, by shaping mine. A few years earlier, at the age of eighty-one, he had married an older woman. Her name was Maude.

I had been coming to see these turtle doves every second weekend for some eight months now, so as to share their gaiety and learn to reason – for Monsieur Ti and his wife were passionate about ideas. Not that they aped the philosophers – far from it: they put their intelligence at the service of laughter, hatching the kind of hoaxes and surprises that unseat rationality. They were in love, Monsieur Ti and Maude – indeed I believe that for him she was *still a woman* – and were persuaded that only the complicity of wild mirth could stave off the decline of passion.

For me they were a stable family, the one I had never known, and I was their son, the one they would never have – in spite of their autumnal ardour.

One Friday, around midnight, I arrived at the wheel of my father's car. Finding the hotel asleep, I went round to the back of the main building. Hidden under a tile, a key let me in to the kitchen. As usual, I double-locked the door behind me. On the kitchen table, a loose sheet of paper left by Maude informed me that room number seven was free. I was starving. I had just opened the fridge and begun to dispatch a terrine of duck when I heard a muffled noise. The tiny sound seemed to be amplified by the quiet of the night.

I put down my knife and went into the hall. A skylight opened. To my consternation, the slight figure of a burglar wormed its way silently and with great agility through the window. I hid behind the reception counter. The shadow left its knapsack on the tile floor and glided towards the lit kitchen.

I moved closer: the intruder had breasts. Judging by her clothes, she had been hitch-hiking. As I watched her I felt a thrill, like the excitement sparked by a master-piece. I was paralysed with timidity. She was perfect, without blemish, and at that moment the light in the hotel endowed her with a radiance I have never seen in anyone else.

She looked about eighteen. Later I learnt that she was twenty. Her physiognomy had that solid, splendidly vigorous grace found only in youth. She was more like

my dreams than those who had inspired them. Never
before had I been able to picture a girl capable of
arousing such desire. She had all the charms my imagination could lend her, and more.

'What are you doing here?' I called, my voice
faltering as I stepped forward into the light.

'And what about you?' she retorted.

She continued in an accusing tone, taking advantage
of my surprise.

'You know, don't you, that patrons aren't supposed
to raid the kitchen?'

'Yeah but . . . but what the hell are you doing here?' I
repeated, pulling myself together.

'This is my home, my grandmother's place.'

'But . . . why did you come in through the window,
like a thief?'

'I've done that ever since I was a child. That's how I
get in when they're not expecting me.'

So, she was Maude's granddaughter.

'Anyway, who's to say that *you're* not the burglar?'
she added roguishly.

I let it drop that Monsieur Ti was a kind of spiritual
father to me and that I had been coming to the hotel regularly these last eight months to drink in his wisdom. Then
she introduced herself as Fanfan and gave me to understand that the elderly Ti was like a grandfather to her too.

She was as amazed as I was, and just as puzzled that Ti
should have been so discreet about our respective exist-
ences: but we made no attempt to clarify this. In all like-
lihood he had been trying to delay the process our
meeting had set in motion.

With her diaphanous brow and transparent complexion,

Fanfan could never hide her feelings; and the ones they now expressed were far from discouraging.

Right from the beginning, our conversation had become tinged with an exquisite ambiguity, and her apparent enjoyment of it was anything but innocent. In these unexpected circumstances, the middle of the night, our meeting had something marvellous about it.

We spoke of our common affection for Monsieur Ti, and it seemed, quite naturally, as if we had always agreed. I was bewitched by her grace and the curves of her figure. At last I had met one of those radiant beings who seem to live only in the world of novels. How must it feel to actually touch a girl like that? was my burning question. Surely, the slightest contact would have brought forth lightning.

Most of all, though, I had the vague sensation that here was the woman who could make me be my true self. In her I recognized the humour and originality of thought that so fascinated me in Monsieur Ti; and in addition, she had all the spontaneity I had lost at Verdelot when I was thirteen.

In the kitchen, the temperature between us remained moderate. Her charms had me in a panic. I hated the thought that she had come to upset the quiet life into which I had locked myself with Laure. And I loathed the unfaithful Alexandre she had awoken within me. Come what may, I would refuse to take orders from the parental chromosomes. And so, with a little help from my willpower, I managed to present a calm expression.

By about three in the morning, with sleep tugging at our eyelids, we came to discuss the question of rooms. Number seven was the only key left on the board.

Trying hard to sound natural, and with an air of feigned detachment, Fanfan suggested we share the room. She saw nothing untoward in the idea since it had two beds. 'After all, we aren't animals, are we?' The false candour with which she uttered this statement had me in turmoil.

But that night I *was* an animal. A lustful beast. Once in room number seven, she began to undress in a sensual slow motion. It was all too much. I watched her discreetly but avidly, drinking in her image. When she loosened her hair, and ruffled it, the sleeves of her blouse rode up her arm to unveil golden flesh radiant with the fullness of the sun.

And yet, to me, this very accumulation of personal charms was a reason for quenching my desire. You may be surprised at my sangfroid, but you must remember that I had several years of mastering my feelings behind me and that, during my adolescence, it had become a reflex to censure my excitement. Besides, I was frightened of betraying Laure.

Already, just caressing Fanfan with my eyes, I felt I was going far enough. Less than a metre from this living masterpiece, lying motionless beneath the blankets, I feasted on her presence.

That night, eyes open in the darkness, ears straining for the slightest sigh from Fanfan – who must surely have thought I was a homosexual – I was overcome by the malarial fever that follows when lovemaking is interrupted just before consummation. I was in an agony of lust, my mind flooding my heart with fervently conceived images. Few of them would have pleased my local curate.

But I had yet to discover just how far the dull drum-beat of desire can lead.

In the morning, Fanfan had gone. Her clothes from the previous night lay scattered around the unmade bed. The urge to smell her blouse was irresistible. I breathed in the odour of her skin, captured in the fibres of the cotton.

Her bed was still warm. She had probably left the room only minutes earlier. I locked the door and, in a kind of daze, slipped between her sheets, into her warmth. The perfumes of our bodies mingled. My rule of conduct remained unbroken, and yet I was enjoying the sensation of sleeping with her – or almost.

I got up only when Fanfan's emanations had evaporated. I was alone again.

Emerging from the room, I nodded a greeting to one of the hotel guests, a man with a face like semolina who was heading for the dining room, and went down to the kitchen.

Fanfan and Monsieur Ti were sitting at the table sipping bowls of coffee and cutting out statistics from a newspaper, then putting them to a lighted match. Gaily they told me of their hatred for any attempt to fasten human destiny in a corset of figures and probabilities. In her vision of things, Fanfan was unique, an anomaly to the laws of mass observation.

She offered me a coffee and stirred me with a smile. As we chatted, she told me of her ambition to be a film director, and nothing less than a giant of the profession. For her, the only way of escaping suffocation by banality was to make films in which life would be shown in its proper fiery colours – not rose-tinted but shocking pink and electric blue.

Fanfan was in a hurry. At the age of seventeen, impatient with the doubts and dithering of adolescence, she had abandoned school, her family and Normandy, and set herself up in Paris, there to make an immediate start on conquering her chosen career.

'You see,' she explained, 'there was an opening. Truffaut had just died.'

'Of course ...'

I didn't know what to make of such candour.

In fact, though Fanfan was surprisingly self-assured, she was neither brazen nor complacent. She could have told me the tallest of tales and I would still have believed her, because what she said and what she was were the same thing. There is nothing more exasperating than the smug and pushy parvenu, but Fanfan held me spellbound.

Racing in pursuit of her thoughts, she spoke so fast that the words seemed to shrink. Her energy thrilled me. Where others saw hills to climb she saw only gentle slopes. Her determination to conquer life's hazards made me feel terribly weak-willed.

Eight days after she left the family fold, her father summoned her back to Normandy and announced that he was cutting her off. Fanfan took it all in her stride and learnt how to sell her photographs to agencies. When, after forcing her way into producers' offices, she was shown the door, Fanfan took her camera by the horns and shot her films in Super 8 on the less-than-super budget scraped together from the sale of fashion photographs. This being insufficient, she had accumulated

15

IOUs with the laboratories and decided that paying her actors was optional. As for her technicians, their remuneration was the pride they were expected to feel at working for her. Not that this made much difference: Fanfan's overdraft was still colossal. Nevertheless, the fact remained that, by the age of twenty, she had made five feature-length films, all in Super 8. '... Including a Western and two fantasy films,' she added proudly.

For the Western, she had made a deal with the owner of a cowboy town built specially for children: she would shoot a commercial for his theme park, and he would lend her the set.

The way she talked, Everest was a knoll, knots were made to be untied and money mattered only to her creditors. Fanfan was not afraid of fear. Her instinct for liberty both fascinated and frightened me. She made me want to jettison my anxieties and live at the altitude of my dreams, and although this desire disturbed me, I knew she was right; 'positive is the only way to think', she liked to say.

Her curiosity and appetite were insatiable. She had a burning desire for self-expenditure, an all-consuming need to reinvent the seventh art. Vitality radiated from the pores of her skin.

There were times, though, when her expression clouded over with cares – the sort that furrow the brow and darken the eyes long after childhood. Her own, as I later found out, had been darkened when her little sister was drowned by the incoming tide. It was Maude and Ti who had reawakened Fanfan's love of life. Fanfan kept quiet about her distress, and there was something deliciously scatterbrained about her which saved her from excess gravity.

That morning, I fell in love with her flaws. She was a liar, but lied only to embellish reality. Her insolence made you laugh. Fanfan was cocky, proud and fer-ociously envious of those who succeeded more quickly than herself, but because she was open about her failings she was never ridiculous. Fanfan was one of those beings whose sins are joyous and whose bad sides have a special grace all of their own. This free spirit dared to be herself, and that was that.

Monsieur Ti poured himself another cup of coffee and recounted his latest dreams, as he did every morning. This exercise in decoding the hieroglyphs and enigmatic scenes secreted by his somnolent brain was one of the great pleasures in his life.

Then it was Fanfan's turn to recount a so-called dream. She gave me a searching look and began:

'I dreamt that some man was chatting me up but would never admit his love, and that the suspense made everything incredibly intense . . .'

Her expression seemed to hint that this was no dream, but a wish that dared not speak its name. Every extra detail confirmed this impression and, in spite of myself, I could feel a violent passion rising up within me for this girl, whose desires were so perfectly in harmony with my own most cherished aspiration: to live in perpetual anticipation, to live an asymptotic love.

She was the woman I had been dreaming of ever since I was thirteen.

Laure's image had suddenly lost its brightness. But my need for stability remained unchanged.

*

At lunch, Fanfan left immediately after the hors d'oeuvre. As Ti explained, she was an avid maker of contacts and rarely turned down an invitation. The result was that she often had three lunches on the same day and at the same time. She hated the idea of being limited to only one existence. She wanted each day to be double or triple.

Ti also revealed the origin of the name Fanfan, for on her birth certificate she was known as Françoise Sauvage. 'Fanfan' did not derive from 'Fran-Fran' – Françoise with a stutter – but had been inspired by the young girl's roguishness, rebelliousness and often-worn black thigh-length boots, three things she shared with the Fanfan La Tulipe of cinematic fame.

And then the sobriquet also carried an echo of 'fawn'; Fanfan did look a bit like a young doe.

Fawnfawn . . . The name obsessed me already.

After lunch I had a call from Laure. She told me about a trick she had played on one of her friends the night before. She had sneaked between the sheets of a girl-friend who lived in a student hostel and waited there until she came to bed; then, after the girl had turned out her bedside lamp, Laure had put her hand on the girl's belly.

Laure laughed as she told me how the girl had leapt up with fear and woken up the whole floor with her shrieking.

Then she asked me how I was doing.

'Fine, fine . . .' I answered.

She whispered a few words of love and hung up.

I felt almost annoyed at Laure's facetiousness. Her gaiety and charm certainly didn't make things any easier for me. Had she been severe, bossy and morose, it would have been easy to leave her for Fanfan. Life with Laure was like going on an entertaining cruise on a calm sea with a delightful woman.

But there was a storm brewing.

I spent the afternoon alone on the beach, deep in passionate thought, obsessed with the implications of Fanfan's barely disguised suggestion.

For the first time in my life, a young woman had expressed a desire identical to the one I had kept bottled up within me for so many years.

I was sorely tempted to fulfil Fanfan's wishes. That way I could preserve the capital of our new-born love while keeping my resolution of lifelong fidelity to Laure. Such a course would mean developing a reflex of restraint, keeping a permanent check on my passions so that Fanfan would never feel sure of my affection.

But I knew my will was weak. If I continued to court this young woman, my determination would inevitably be sapped and then founder, fatally. How could I hope to resist the raging desire that would assail me in her magnetic presence?

Sooner or later – and perhaps sooner than I imagined – I would succumb to the temptation of my senses.

Nevertheless, this idea of constantly postponing my romantic vows was a tempting one. I felt a powerful sympathy with the courtly lovers of yore who dedicated their lives to one fair damsel: their restraint was the measure of their virility, and their conquest of carnal appetite the proof of their attachment.

The plan so cleverly suggested by Fanfan flattered my penchant for novelistic living. As a child I had been fascinated by historic figures who managed to imbue their destinies with the aura of fiction. My library was full of biographies of men of state and women of power whom I dreamed of joining in the history books. The day I went up to Sciences-Po I could feel the watchful eye of my future biographer upon me. Two months later, I had reached the sad conclusion that my conception of politics was an extremely literary one, and that the establishment prepared you not for heroism but for a career. Disillusionment strengthened my desire to put a literary gloss on my daily deeds. With Laure, my aim was an easy life; but I still needed my complementary share of passion.

Now it seemed to me that the only way of encountering the unexpected was to enter into Fanfan's so-called dream. Perhaps it was mad to try to postpone the moment of pleasure *ad infinitum*, but reason struck me as singularly lacking when set against sentiment. I was tempted by the vertigo of unfailing passion.

If I made this choice, then my every thought would be to intensify the inclination Fanfan appeared to feel for me and prolong the pregnant preludes to love. Your prospects seem so fine when you are waiting for the letter of release, and the moment of opening it is rich with promise: but life never keeps its word and the vista of unending happiness is a *trompe-l'oeil* on the wall of the present. I was happy with Laure, but I no longer quivered with anticipation at the thought of being with her again, as I did in our wooing days.

Still, I couldn't see myself, day in day out, fighting back those unconscious urges which batter down our best resolutions. At twenty, you cannot repress your impulses forever.

I therefore deemed it prudent to beat a retreat the next morning, as planned, and steer clear of this girl who had upset my well-ordered little world. Yes, I hated Fanfan for her spontaneity and the carefree way she ran her life. If only she had been less beautiful and less true, her radiance less solar. I abhorred the passions she made me feel. No, Verdelot was not my spiritual home. I was reasonable, faithful to Laure, serious about study, thrifty, sober. I preferred to forget this ambassadress of liberty, this young woman for whom life was one long summer holiday.

However, I still had an evening and a night to spend under the same roof.

When I next saw Fanfan it was dusk. She arrived at the hotel in a white lace outfit that emphasized the perfection of her figure. Fanfan's was not one of those flat and featureless bodies that drive the caressing hand to despair; no, hers was full and rounded, but always on the right side of plump.

She had decided to show us some film from her latest shoot. Her every expression and gesture was alive with roguish intelligence as she set about mounting her Super 8 projector on its tripod, but there was none of the smug self-assurance that often accompanies striking beauty. I saw the soft curves of her waist and caught my breath. I

21

ached to possess her as my eyes roamed furtively but avidly over her body.

Maude and Monsieur Ti sat themselves in armchairs in the front row and I took up position on a wicker sofa behind them. Fanfan turned out the lights.

Terrifying images filled the screen. War had broken out in the room. In a muddy, rat-infested trench, a touching friendship had sprung up between two soldiers of what looked like southern European origin. The realism of it all was quite stunning. The actors moved from sequence to sequence as in a genuine war, trampling corpses underfoot with weary detachment. The cast was remarkable, the backgrounds as meticulously orchestrated as the foregrounds. The whole thing carried a powerful emotional impact. Amazed at the strength of the story, I wondered how Fanfan could have created such an effect on so skeletal a budget. But then she switched on the lights again.

'Now for the surprise,' she proclaimed. 'This is only a first edit. Wait until I change the reel.'

'Where did you shoot it?' murmured Monsieur Ti.

'In the Iran-Iraq war, on the Iraqi side,' she said, juggling with the cans of film.

'But how did you get to the Front?!'

She shrugged.

'Like everything else. You negotiate.'

I imagined the trouble a woman must run into in a country both Islamic and belligerent, but the way she presented things, it seemed the main problem was adapting the script to the movements of the armies and getting decent lighting on the Front.

'You can't imagine the fixes I got into,' she sighed.

22

The impecunious Fanfan had persuaded herself that the only way to film war well was to share the risks facing the combatants. Television reporting struck her as inadequate, though. As she saw it, filming the war properly meant introducing into reality the slight discrepancy provided by fiction, without which what looks like factual presentation is actually a lie. Fanfan believed that while poets may flirt with truth, mathematicians can never be more than exact.

Now, I can understand that you might suspect I'm making all this up, because it is pretty hard to believe that a twenty-year-old girl with a camera under her arm could slip into the middle of such a bloody conflict. And yet it's true: that was where Fanfan shot her film. I would never have dared imagine something so unlikely, but the reels she had brought back proved it. Fanfan was one of those women whose charm is due in part to the extraordinary lives they lead. She was of the same race as Mata Hari, Alexandra David-Neel, Cleopatra, or my mother.

Her daring, her total commitment to her art, her cheerful grace – everything about this girl was attractive.

At dinner, she blandly informed me that she was wont to come back down to the kitchen when everyone else was in bed to finish off the leftovers, and that her appetite usually stirred around midnight.

That night, Maude had found us separate rooms. A customer – semolina-face – had left.

Fanfan's allusion to her nocturnal eating habits sounded very much like an invitation.

*

23

Midnight approached and I lay alone in my room. None of the novels I tried could allay my longing to be with Fanfan. Yet the other half of me kept saying that if I let myself get carried away and declared my feelings, then I could kiss goodbye to the heady delights of amorous foreplay; and those moments when desire is somehow suspended are surely the very honey of love. Besides, I was frightened at the idea of betraying Laure. The spectre of Verdelot refused to go away.

It was torture.

In the end, I decided to go down and see her. I had to learn to silence my lust and disguise it as mere friendship. Had I not already done so time and time again in the years before I met Laure? Yes, but what worried me was that I should actually need to remind myself of this fact. In the end, though, I went, swearing that this would be the last time. I had decided to leave the hotel the following morning and had resolved never to see Fanfan again.

For one exquisite moment on the stairs, I steeled my mind and assumed an air of detachment, glazing my eyes with just a touch of indifference.

I held my breath and opened the kitchen door. I was almost fainting. The room was empty. I had to face the bitter truth: the thoughts I had attributed to Fanfan were merely my own dreams.

I was reflecting on this when I noticed a light in the lounge that adjoined the kitchen. I went nearer. Fanfan was sitting cross-legged on the carpet, her body slack and relaxed. She was hunched over a magazine, scraping mechanically at some scraps of *gratin* with a fork. She was wearing a fine cotton T-shirt and very short shorts; and nothing more.

The moment I saw her I felt the convulsions of lust starting up again. In an attempt to retain my self-control, I looked away and forced a little firmness into my voice: 'Oh, I didn't think you'd be here.'

'Weren't you asleep?' she asked, amazed to see me.

'I must have had too much coffee.'

The tone of these opening exchanges was disorientating. It was as if she had no idea of the fire she had ignited. But I sensed it was all a ploy. The effect of her coolness was only to make me even more agitated.

Gradually, our exchanges grew warmer. God knows how, but we started talking about our ideas of love. Providentially enough, these were identical. We both refused to accept the precarious nature of ordinary feelings and the cooling of passion. Our two souls were united in their rejection of mediocrity. By now I was all aquiver, unable to keep my eyes off the breasts floating free under her T-shirt and those naked legs; and judging by the tone of her voice she was no longer as indifferent to my presence as she had been at the beginning of our rambling discussion. At times she even looked at me the way people do when speaking straight from the heart. Everything about her betrayed the advent of a violent attraction.

Our mutual understanding was so marvellous that in the excitement of our exchange we failed to notice the passing time. Bit by bit, she began to loosen up, reveal her true feelings. The more she revealed, the stronger my conviction grew that here was the love of my life. With her I could allow myself to be sincere, just as I could with Monsieur Ti. My false gaiety dissolved. I no longer needed to try so hard just to be liked. She was delighted with my new-found spontaneity. Now, as I told her about my family, I felt no need to dress up the facts. Suddenly, the simple reality seemed sufficient. Laure had never made it easy for me to be myself. In her company I cheated, as I did with everyone else.

At about two a.m., Fanfan started talking about her professional worries. The lack of confidence shown by producers wounded her more than she dared admit.

Her distress moved me. Almost involuntarily, I squeezed her hand. She quivered. My gesture made her breathless.

This was the moment Monsieur Ti chose to enter the room, his dressing gown bound tightly round him. The sudden interruption clipped the wings of our intimacy.

'Aren't you cold?' he asked. 'The heating's gone off again.'

And he disappeared into the cellar to put it back on.

Now I knew for certain. Unless I retreated at this very instant, it would only be a matter of time before I was unfaithful to Laure. The thought made me panic. I could see the dreaded Alexandre Crusoé being reborn in Fanfan's arms. Retreating from this chaotic vision, I gave a worried glance at my watch and offered the late hour as an excuse for returning hurriedly to my room.

Stretched out on my bed, I swore I would keep away from Fanfan for ever.

THREE

THE FOLLOWING WEEKEND, LAURE BEGGED ME TO GO
with her to her parents' place in Orléans. She tempted
and cajoled me and insisted that I had to go because
Monsieur and Madame Chantebise would be celebrating
their twenty-five years of non-divorce that very
Saturday. I found the idea of having to rejoice because
they had managed to 'hold out' together in the same
bed for a quarter of a century pretty depressing, but this
time the trip could not be avoided. I had already backed
out of these visits a good dozen times to run off to
Maude and Monsieur Ti. One more refusal would have
meant a scene with Laure.

The dull, monotonous existence of the Chantebises
was merely a poor imitation of happiness but, much to
my annoyance, they nevertheless considered themselves
fortunate. Rumour had it that they had discovered the

27

secret of inexhaustible attachment, and their friends took their constancy for fidelity – when in fact it was only immobility.

Like many others, Daddy de Chantebise purchased household peace in the currency of concession: he let his wife govern him. She scolded him when he put two sugars in his coffee, chose his boxer shorts, imposed the statutory muffler in winter and regulated the visits of 'outsiders' to their manor in Orléans. He only said 'no' to her when 'no' was what she wanted to hear. In general – and because he didn't dare shout out 'for God's sake, be quiet!' – a meekly murmured 'yes' was his answer. Too timorous to admit to any desire – except perhaps for a boiled egg at breakfast – he resigned himself to her tyranny with the sighs of the defeated male. It was out of this same anxiety to avoid domestic conflict that he consented to wear 'indoor clothes' – the veritable uniform of the tamed husband, comprising knitted cardigan, limp trousers and shiny slippers.

Monsieur de Chantebise's only talent was for disguising his stupidity. This wavering, pusillanimous cipher spent most of the day in a mild torpor, assuming a pensive manner so as to mask the void within. He spoke little, but when he did he quoted copiously from the great authors, managing to steer judiciously clear of the border between culture and pedantry. His greatest fear was to be taken by surprise. What little wit he had was consumed in striving to produce an effect of thoughtfulness. He was a barrister who had never pleaded, a bibliophile who rarely read – and, I imagine, a husband most moderate in bed. It was almost as if he merely pretended to exist.

Like his ancestors, Daddy de Chantebise professed an utter disdain for work. The allowance granted by his mother-in-law afforded him ample leisure to cultivate his native indolence.

As for his wife, she devoted her energies to keeping the conjugal fires burning and to this effect donned girlish frocks that were supposed to bring out her blushing maidenly beauty. Had her charms been a fraction riper she would merely have looked ridiculous. She was a caustic woman with an ironic, distant manner, but happy to lash out whenever her husband needed to be humiliated for an excess of inanity.

The Chantebises held themselves in great veneration. Those without Chantebise blood in their veins were barely worth looking down on. Invitations were issued to friends only in exceptional circumstances, and socializing was generally limited to close relations. Laure's younger sisters were their mother's best friends, and I was admitted only as a future son-in-law.

Laure was the first to laugh at her family: she knew full well that her mother and father had smothered their youthful passion. But criticism from me was intolerable. One ironic comment and she leapt to their defence.

We arrived in Orléans for dinner and went straight to table. The dining room groaned under its wood panelling, lavish gilding and portraits of ancestors, most of whom had been killed in the ranks of the Ancien Régime or had lost touch with their heads during the Revolution. Besides these bewigged and frame-frozen ancestors, our company included Laure's three younger – and pretty much alive – sisters, a hunched old aunt who hobbled about with the aid of a walking frame, and the de Chantebise parents.

The meal was torture. This family made provincials look cosmopolitan. The entire conversation consisted of threadbare anecdotes, petty backstabbing of distant cousins and noxious rumours based on hearsay. Then came the climax of our evening – the joyless celebration of twenty-five years' conjugal *ennui* by means of a mauve-coloured cake that was, it went without saying, delicious.

At this juncture our sad gathering was spiced up by a moment of family drama. Monsieur Chantebise gave his wife a silver cake server – the same present as two years earlier. In spite of his mumbled excuses, her sarcasm soon exploded into rage:

'Maurice, you've got a Brillo pad where your brain should be!' she screeched. This daring metaphor naturally missed its target, being well above Maurice's toupee-covered head.

Next on the agenda was the statutory visit to 'Madame Mère', the mother of Madame de Chantebise – their Saturday obligation. I was exasperated by the way this family corseted time into strict routines, and the quickfire condemnations or snide backhanders that were the speciality of this ninety-one-year-old bitch made their devotion look even more absurd. This harridan of a mother-in-law loved to lash with faint praise, and if ever she made you an authentic compliment it was sure to contain an invidious comparison aimed at humiliating someone else. Monsieur de Chantebise was her favourite target and, were it not for his wife's insistence, would gladly have abstained from visiting. Instead, he had spent twenty years of Saturday afternoons paying his respects with a mixture of courage and cowardice. As for me, lunch had been all I could stomach. I had no intention of going to kiss the hand of this viper in old lady's clothing.

Laure reproached me bitterly for wanting to 'go it alone'. Her upbringing amidst these gregarious creatures made stepping out of the family line inconceivable, but I was driven by the fear of ending up on a lead, like my future father-in-law. I therefore parried my companion's injunctions, picked up my bag and slipped away as discreetly as I could.

The spectacle of this fossilized family, this rigid Chantebise couple, was even more terrifying than that of my own manic parents. On my way back to the station, I realized with a shock that beneath my conformist aspirations there lay an indomitably passionate and excessive inner self. My dream of peaceful married life was based on a misunderstanding. I was a true Crusoé, even if my path would be different from my mother's and my father's. I had to find a way of satisfying both my thirst for excitement and my need for order.

During the train ride to Paris, I resolved to take the biggest risk any sexed being can take. I decided that I would see Fanfan again, yet remain within the bounds of friendship: passionate outpourings would be constantly deferred. This self-imposed decree thrilled me. It was the guarantee that my craving for Fanfan would never decline, that we would never descend to the platitudes of the average couple.

At the same time, I wanted to secure my union with Laure. The idea of breaking off with her plunged me

31

into the nightmare of Verdelot. I needed our relationship to keep me balanced; besides, there was nothing unpleasant about sharing daily existence with Laure.

To seduce Fanfan without succumbing: that was now my maxim.

This book is the story of my struggle to act on it. Every day I had to do battle with my feelings in the fight not to weaken. To break these iron chains would have meant endangering my emotional stability. Never before had I had so many sleepless nights. Fanfan was the name of my torment. I could not love her freely, nor could I love another or live without loving her.

If I refuse to anticipate the outcome of my inner struggle here and now, it is not to arouse my reader's curiosity, but because at the end of the long road of desire I came upon the unexpected: intimations of great things.

FOUR

MONSIEUR TI WAS CARVED FROM THE SAME RARE WOOD as Fanfan. He was one of those liberty-loving creatures who revolt against what the majority consider inevitable.

The legend went that Ti never paid his taxes. In fact, I rather suspect that he did release just enough lucre to give the tax man temporary satisfaction. Then, when the functionary became too avid, he presumably condescended to meet him, receiving the uncomfortable collector with that air of superiority he could never hide, pretending to be bedridden. Or he would attempt to disappear by publishing a death notice in the obituary pages of the local paper.

In keeping with the same principles, Monsieur Ti never resigned himself to insuring his car and his little hotel. According to his philosophy, a free man does not take out insurance. The possible consequences and inevitable tussles with the authorities were neither here nor there. His dignity was not negotiable.

Likewise, Ti never acknowledged the right of Paris to control time, and refused to obey the government diktat imposing winter and summer hours that ran ahead of the sun. Nature was his clock and the sun his time-keeper. When it was two o'clock in Paris on 14 July, the clock in Monsieur Ti's hotel struck twelve; and patrons hoping to eat a hot meal were advised to be there at Ti-time – although this law could sometimes be bent for regulars. Strangely enough, Ti's intransigence was good for business at the Hôtel du Globe. Ti and Maude had numerous patrons who came specially to spend a few days in harmony with nature.

Monsieur Ti had gone against his libertarian principles only once: for love.

The Ti I came to know was a man who felt no great desire to linger on in life. True, there were days when he seemed untouched by old age, as if it had forgotten him, and his arms were like thick new shoots, strong enough to stay death's scythe. But Ti hated the dwindling and defeats that come with old age – he was sick of struggling against the compression of his long spinal column, which he had always used to the full to maintain what he considered an appropriate bearing.

The idea of being responsible for his own death did not upset his convictions. On the contrary, as a free man, he wanted to choose the time of his going. But Ti loved Maude and Maude loved life, even when it dragged its feet. She would never have followed him to the grave. Ti therefore accepted his own decline so that he could watch over her, and spare her the torments of another widowhood.

Monsieur Ti was a man of uncompromising temperament. He was constantly asserting his personality,
surpassing himself with each new day and refusing to let
life be lived without striving for the best. I was lucky: the
hotel took up little of his time, and in the idle moments
of his retirement he allowed me to come and converse
with him. Usually, he answered my questions with questions. When I pressed my point he replied promptly but
flippantly on the essential issue. His method was to
throw you off-balance. He strove to be light-hearted,
aiming at the detachment of those who use laughter and
irony to keep life at a distance. He had nothing but
sarcasm for the po-faced would-be sage.

Ti's intelligence revealed my own lack of finesse; but
he was a master at raising his interlocutor to his own
level. My intellectual reflexes were moulded by his. He
made me feel I had conquered myself.

Not that Ti was fooled by my masks. He saw right
through my air of probity, humility and courage to my falseness, my petty vanity and my cowardice. I had no choice
but to be myself, and it was an obligation I appreciated.

Ti was a contradictory old fellow; although he envied
those who went through life unscathed, in permanent
harmony with themselves, he was maddened by my
desire not to get too involved. 'If you don't pay the
price, then life won't deliver the goods,' he kept muttering.

In fact, a guru was the last thing I was looking for
when I started going to Ti's hotel. What I was seeking
was a spot of fornication. Before I met Laure, the Globe
was where I spent dirty weekends with the girls I had,
alas, been weak enough to kiss. It was cheap, and I loved
its timbered façade; in addition, on the ground floor, the

35

Hôtel du Globe had an admirable blue porcelain lava-
tory where I liked to meditate or read, my briefs around
my ankles and my sphincters at ease.

As the weekends wore on, gobbling up the money I
earnt by hiring out my profile on film sets, I found
myself spending more and more time in the hotel bar,
raising my right arm with the enigmatic Monsieur Ti.
His immobility was like an injunction to silence. His every
assertion was carefully considered, and I was fascinated
by the freedom of his opinions and the range of his insights.
He had answers aplenty and I was full of questions.

The face of this old buzzard was a blank page – or,
rather, so dense with contradiction as to be illegible. His
forehead was a tangle of lines and his cheeks seemed to
have been hollowed out by great suffering, yet Ti's
physiognomy was unbowed. His sharp, wilful nose issued
a constant challenge to the coming day.

It intrigued me that nothing betrayed his origins. He
seemed to have erased his background, although I am
not so sure he ever had one.

He was learning to die and I was learning to live, but
we were both seekers and shared a common anxiety.

The day came when my mistresses were mere pre-
texts for my weekly return to the hotel. In the end I
dispensed with this pretence and gradually became a full
member of my elected, octogenarian family. I realized
that they had come to count on my presence the
evening Monsieur Ti opened the Bible – a book he
rarely consulted – to read me 'the return of the prodigal
son'. No commentary was made and none needed.

Maude had reached that time in a woman's life when
she can once again admit to her date of birth. She was

eighty-seven, and at ease with every year. She used all the refinements of a woman's toilette to maintain her feminine charm. And when it came to beauty, Maude was above average for her age.

Maude measured people not by their deeds but by the weight of their souls. Great vices, exceptional transparency or sublime virtues touched her more than any exploit. She never asked about people's professions, as if these were mere disguises. She was more interested in exploring their dreams, their tastes and their inclinations.

I came to a better understanding of her love of life when I realized that every morning she got up at dawn to go and watch the sun rise over the sea, standing on the dyke that had been built opposite their hotel. She watched as the gap grew between the horizon and the daystar, then returned to bed. Sometimes Monsieur Ti accompanied her in his dressing gown. On the deserted beach he squeezed Maude's arm, donned his glasses and felt just that little bit younger.

In their hotel, Monsieur Ti and Maude employed a cantankerous and rustic Norman, a real dragon of a woman known to all and sundry as Hermantrude. I never found out if that was her real name. Cruel chromosomes had made her into a meaty, masculine hulk devoid of charm. I suppose her ancestors must have begun drinking to her arrival as early as the Middle Ages. Her features included a vocal organ capable of waking the dead, a whinnying laugh and two tiny tits flapping listlessly on a flat chest. Her skull was covered with moist, flaccid skin which overflowed to form a fine, toad-like throat. Her reddened eyelids had the greatest difficulty closing. Her vocal orifice had the same problem, and her lips were like two lush slugs. Though her hair was her own, she did insist on dyeing it a bright rust colour every fort-night. People assumed she was simple, for her gargoyle features had only three different permutations. One of these expressed animal contentment, another a disturbing (and no doubt unexercised) lewdness, while the third bespoke stifled rage. She was a passionate collector of exotic postcards, and when she gazed at these radiant images of other lands her mutant counte-nance took on an almost human quality.

Walking with me on the sea wall amidst the swirling seagulls, Ti would delve into his past, weaving together whatever episodes he was willing to revive, patiently dredging up dozens of anecdotes from his memory.

He had acquired a taste for hoaxes when, as a young surgeon, he joined the Resistance. In fact, 'Monsieur Ti' was his operational pseudonym. He had hung onto it after the Liberation, casting aside his real name: Jardin.

The constant risk of torture and firing squads prompted Ti to combat his fear by playing tricks both on his companions and on the occupying forces. There was always an absurd, even humorous element in his actions. They called him 'Doctor Ha-ha'. His comrades thought him facetious. Only little Marcel had seen the contour of terror beneath the curve of his smile. The two men had been captured, tortured and deported to Buchen-wald and then Langenstein, places which make the word horror a mere euphemism. Marcel was seventeen, Ti was twenty-six. He had made the mistake of letting some German prisoners out onto the streets of a small town, clothed only by a helmet on their heads and a funnel on their genitals. This pathetic prank was his way of saying to the Germans, 'Come on, it's all a big joke!', of denying danger, the better to live with it. The funnels were his downfall. Interrogated by the Gestapo, the supplier talked. Ti never spoke about his deportation. One evening, however, he admitted that in the midst of the camps he had stopped joking and, with a movement of the lips that was much more eloquent than any words, he told me that little Marcel never came back.

After the war Monsieur Ti left Europe, returning to Ker Emma in Normandy only twenty-seven years later. His family assumed he was dead. He never mentioned those years when he wandered deep into the heart of the wide world, though it would have been a relief to let the words out. The memories that haunted him were more than one man could bear.

I must now tell you about Ker Emma, that unique spot, that dream come true, my dream. For you cannot understand Monsieur Ti, Maude and Fanfan without knowing about this Breton-sounding Norman village.

Ker Emma is like a family, a family village of a thousand souls.

It all started in 1853 when one Népomucène Sauvage committed the dowry of his young Breton wife, Emma, to the construction of a dyke which, he hoped, would close off the bay and enable him to dry out its eight hundred and fifty hectares. When he had completed this undertaking the State expressed its gratitude by giving him the land he had won back from the waves.

Népomucène was a loving husband. He christened the newly emerged land 'Ker Emma', and gave his wife seventeen offspring. Three of these only lived long enough to receive the unction of baptism. The other fourteen made their homes in Ker Emma in accordance with the wishes of old Népomucène, whose dream it was that the family tree planted by his love for Emma should put down permanent roots there.

More than a century later, Ker Emma is home to some thousand descendants of Emma and Népomucène Sauvage. When a house goes up for sale it is kept for a member of the clan. The inhabitants deposit their money with the family bank, the Sea Wall Bank, and deflowering is the prerogative of distant cousins – though marriage between first cousins is, of course, forbidden. Ker Emma also has its own retirement home, which Ti naturally despises, and a Council of the Elders which watches over both the moral unity of this strange tribe and the maintenance of the sea wall.

Each inhabitant knows that he or she is the descendant of an extraordinary love and a great dream.

The granite dyke is the key to Ker Emma. Without it, Monsieur Ti would never have come back from Buchenwald. It is Fanfan's backbone.

This wall taught the people of Ker Emma never to give up. Three times – in 1894, 1928 and 1972 – it was shattered by the great winter tides. And three times it was rebuilt.

On the first of July, the anniversary of the inauguration of the first dyke, the folk of Ker Emma dance on the wall of 1972 to celebrate their victory over the ocean, their pride at being different. They thank the sea wall for giving them the strength to assert their spiritual and financial power; for Ker Emma is home to a number of flourishing companies, all built with the support of the Sea Wall Bank.

FANFAN

In 1976, prompted by Ti's influence and by the desire to preserve its naturally harmonious way of life, Ker Emma rejected summer and winter time. Having spent one hundred and twenty-three years struggling against the Atlantic, they were not about to be intimidated by Paris. Ker Emma is thus the only village in France to live by solar time. When the post office clock says ten in the morning, it is eleven or noon in the rest of the country. When it comes to opening or closing the voting booths, the Town Hall is a law unto itself. And to enable its inhabitants to watch TV without staying up too late, the village records the programmes and broadcasts them the next day on the local cable network, starting at eight-thirty, local time.

If I had resolved never to express my passion for Fanfan, it was because my contacts with this clan had made me a son of the sea wall too. Without it, I would never have believed in the power of the will over the senses, in my own capacity to dam for all eternity the waves of wild thoughts that crashed against my mind whenever I was with Fanfan in mind or in body.

Monsieur Ti returned in 1972. The sea wall had just given way for the third time. Though already bent with age, Ti joined in the reconstruction work. He felt he was regenerating his identity.

Up to that point, Ti had always been a solitary traveller on the road of life. But then in the cemetery of Ker Emma – a favoured haunt where he could defy death in its own back yard – he met an aged and happy woman. As she polished her husband's tombstone she told him of her joy in life and offered him some vitamin C tablets. Her name was Maude Sauvage.

41

They started seeing each other. He marvelled at her capacity for wonder. And, one night, as they were leaving the cemetery, he kissed her fervently with the reassuring thought that before their passion could wane they would be back in the cemetery – feet first.

Monsieur Ti execrated the decline of love. For him, the lassitude to which so many couples resign themselves was a shameful defeat. He had never been tempted by marriage. He had always refused to tow or be in tow.

Maude was wise enough not to make any claims on him. Simply, and with the assurance that comes of living in harmony with one's ideas, she showed him that there can be no passionate tenderness without some kind of commitment. Such was the kind of relationship she had known with her late husband. Three weeks later, jealous of this past figure of perfection, Monsieur Ti had popped a ring on her finger. She was eighty-three, two years his senior.

Old man Ti threw himself into this matrimonial adventure only because he knew time was on his side. He would be spared the mundane. His marriage would conserve the ineffable savour of their nascent passion. The charm would never wear off.

Fanfan and I were only twenty. Between us and death stood half a century, maybe more. If I failed to quell my appetites, then the dangers of mummification would be legion. I saw only one solution: to make the anticipation of our first kiss perpetual. Half a century of expectation, that was my dream.

But Fanfan's figure promised infinite delights. As my loins kept reminding me, she looked like the sort of girl who did it in technicolour.

FIVE

INSTEAD OF GOING HOME AFTER MY WEEKEND IN
Orléans I went to the Alps to pick an edelweiss for
Fanfan. I wanted to do something to prove the strength
of my passion, and to make my refusal to kiss her seem
even more disconcerting.

This was all very calculating, but I was totally sincere.

I was overcome with joy as the train neared the Alps.
I felt I was a character in a novel, escaping routine
behaviour. I couldn't stop smiling. At last, I was liberated from bourgeois love.

In the bar I met some students who were talking
about reaching the peak of Mont Blanc the very next
day. As I asked them about their expedition we struck
up a superficial friendship, and we continued swapping
banalities until one of them asked where I was going.

'I'm going up a mountain to pick an edelweiss for the girl I love,' I replied enthusiastically.

'Your girlfriend?' asked one of the girls in astonishment.

'No, I love her too much to even touch her.'

They thought I was kidding.

'No, where are you really going?'

'It's true, I swear.'

It took me half an hour to convince them that the aim of my trip really was to pluck an edelweiss for my love, and yet another half hour for them to accept that I had no intention of sweeping this girl I loved and who loved me into my arms. Sixty minutes later, then, I had all the men staring at me as if I were some kind of extraterrestrial. Still, the girls didn't all seem to find my behaviour so hopelessly old-fashioned.

I tried to convince the men that my line of conduct was profoundly necessary, but in spite of these energetic protestations, they just mocked and mocked. It was all extremely wounding, and I started getting sarcastic. These young people seemed unaware that man was created with the sole purpose of loving women, and that only in passion can he attain the sublime. Without love, men are just puppets moved by futile desires. Life without love is a life in two dimensions.

When I left them a few hours later at Chamonix station I felt certain of the beauty of my undertaking. They watched me go with puzzled faces. Then I heard a low masculine voice: 'Well there's a fruitcake for you.' To which a girl's voice riposted: 'Well when was the last time you gave me flowers?'

This short exchange strengthened my resolve still

44

further. Whatever the cost, I had to find that edelweiss for Fanfan. At first, my quest had been like a mad obsession – extravagant but exciting too. Now it seemed like an act decreed by reason and ratified by common sense. It is the people who are half-hearted about their passions who are mad.

It was around eleven in the morning when the bus dropped me by the cable car. I went straight to the ticket kiosk:

'Do you know where I can find some edelweiss?'

'They're protected flowers; picking is prohibited.' And the man pointed to a poster with photographs of plants that the Ministry of the Environment hoped to save from the bouquet madness of tourists.

I squirmed, but went ahead and requested a ticket for the cable car. The man insisted:

'I warn you, the gendarmes will fine you.'

I shrugged and got into the cabin, which began to gain altitude. I really did feel bad about attacking nature, but I hadn't come hundreds of kilometres just for the view.

Fortunately, there was no gendarme waiting to stir my guilt feelings when I got out of the cable car. By now the weather was getting hot and I was thirsty. I drank the froth from a mountain stream and set off for the peak with a light tread, as if borne along by the image of Fanfan.

Three hours later what I had picked up was not an edelweiss but a diarrhoea as fast as the gushing stream from which I should never have drunk. My guts had turned to liquid. This bodily treason, at the very moment when I needed all my strength for the climb,

45

confirmed my belief that only the mind is trustworthy. My will was made of iron.

But, at about six in the evening, after many harrowing hours of running around in the mountains, I felt even this conviction abandoning me as, abetted by my sloshing gut and raging hunger, doubt wormed its way into my mind. My quest suddenly seemed stupid. What on earth was I doing there, squatting on this over-size rock? Now I knew why the students had smirked like that. I realized that it was a waste of time and energy to try and live your life like a character in a novel. True, my first step in this business justified the second, but it was best to call off this hare-brained act of chivalry and sensibly go back, back to Laure's bed to lie down.

I rose to go. Weariness gave way to stupefaction: there in front of me was an edelweiss. This cottony flower countered all the cowardly thoughts I had allowed into my mind. Suddenly, all my doubts eva-porated. This unhoped-for discovery taught me that if I only persevered then all the promises I had made in making my resolution would be kept.

Softly, with infinite gentleness, I picked the edelweiss, laid it in a paper cone, and set off back for Paris.

Laure had been getting worried about my disappear-ance. She wanted to know exactly what had been going on. I lied and rejoiced in it, as if I really did have a mistress, really was Fanfan's lover. Of course, I was afraid to make this desire a reality, but I did enjoy acting as if the crucial step had been taken.

Though Laure was willing to believe my over-the-top explanations, she was less understanding when I refused

to spend the next weekend back at her parents' place.
'Right, then, I'll go on my own!'
Little did she know she was giving me carte blanche
to see Fanfan.
'All right,' I said, doing my best not to smile.

And so I arranged to meet Fanfan on Saturday night
and reserved the best table in a small restaurant on the
north bank of the Marne, twenty kilometres out of Paris.
At night the terrace, which overlooked the river, was
candle-lit, a place of water and shadows – almost a love
declaration in its own right.

My plan was to lay siege to Fanfan's feelings but never
be explicit. This meant showing sustained and sugges-
tive interest while undermining it with various 'telltale'
phrases or slips. I wanted the evening to be a subtle
blend of frustration and intense expectation.

You may find this premeditated behaviour surprising;
after all, lovers are supposed to go with the flow of their
passions, aren't they? Sure. But I have always been both
calculating and sincere. Yes, my approach would be
tactical but my aim would be true. I had a genuine
passion for the games of love, and I have never played
them without intense emotion.

Besides, there was no guarantee that I would behave
as intended. It was easy enough to plan my attitudes
when Fanfan wasn't around, but putting plans into
action was another kettle of fish altogether. There was
always a risk that just seeing her might paralyse my willpower. Yet I believed myself capable of tempering my
emotions. I had to.

My resolve strengthened as our dinner came nearer,
not least because of my constantly growing feeling of

47

shame at the thought that merely preparing for this meeting was in itself a betrayal of Laure. And yet I couldn't say I lusted after Fanfan. For although we cannot be held responsible for our desires, I was, theoretically, in control of my actions. I thought that if I abstained from kissing Fanfan I would redeem what I felt to be a sin. Such are the strange deals made between self and conscience.

But then, as I said, I had no idea whether my conduct would follow my resolution.

At eight o'clock on Saturday evening I was outside Fanfan's home, trembling at the wheel of my father's car. She swept onto the street in a sculptured strapless dress which outlined each exquisite curve.

Seeing her, I blurted out, 'Excuse me, but I just have to relieve myself' – which I did – and dashed off to the nearest urinal. There I took in hand the throbbing desire provoked by her appearance. The pleasure was paltry, I admit, but my need was great.

Having regained my composure I was able to go back and open the car door for her, like those rare young men who still practise old-fashioned gallantry. I murmured a compliment as she settled into her seat.

At the restaurant, my fingers brushed her skin as I removed her shawl. I sat her facing the Marne and suggested a menu.

'My favourite dishes!'

'I know,' I whispered. And I did, having cross-examined her grandmother on the subject over the phone that afternoon.

Ever the perfect escort, I twice asked the waiter to change her melon. I also offered to have her films shown to one of my father's producer friends. She looked at me as if I had changed winter for summer with a wave of my wand. I wanted her to feel that in my company life was a dream come true.

She talked at length about her childhood and told me how her sister's drowning had thrown a pall over the family's happiness. I listened in fascinated silence to the story of these formative experiences, knowing this would give her the impression that I understood her completely. Then she spoke about her adolescence and her romantic aspirations, and the unwelcome attentions with which boys had answered them. By which she meant groping. Her subtle allusions showed me how much she appreciated my own delicacy. She continued:

'Perhaps they were like that with me because I never wear any knickers.'

What could I say? Nothing. I was stunned. I wasn't expecting such a direct attack. So, she was naked under that dress.

'You see,' she went on, 'that's what's so extraordinary about film. Just one line of dialogue and the whole scene changes. Don't worry – I am wearing knickers. I was joking.'

Looking out over the Marne, she pursued her theme of dialogue in film. But whenever, as she often did, she turned to look at me and our gazes met, there was a passion in our eyes that more than made up for the restraint of our conversation. I had to look away or cool my senses and my heart with a glass of cold water.

Every second counted for Fanfan, existence itself was a thrilling sensation. In her company I was learning to enjoy life's moments of stillness. She was civilizing me.

After a long silence, I finally produced the edelweiss I had taken such pains to pick.

'What is it, a daisy?'

'No,' I said, piqued. 'An edelweiss.'

'A real one?'

'Yes.'

'But they're extremely rare!'

'I went to pick it for you last Sunday, above Chamonix.'

'Are you taking the piss?'

Fanfan liked to spice her impeccable diction with a dash of vulgarity.

'If you won't believe me, then no one will. Still, I can't force you to.'

For a moment Fanfan was bemused, then she smiled and, with a precipitation that betrayed her emotion, took my hand. But the squeeze I gave was that of a businessman who has just clenched a deal. I smiled and said heartily, 'I did it to seal our new friendship. True friendship with a woman is such a wonderful thing.'

'Of course,' she stammered.

Confusion clouded her eyes and seemed to make her dizzy. How could Fanfan, of all people, Fanfan who could charm anyone she wanted, understand when a man was anything less than fascinated by her?

'Something wrong?' I murmured sweetly.

'No . . . no.'

I apologized and left the table, as if to go to the men's room. Then when we left and she offered to pay her half of the bill I told her it had already been settled.

I helped her on with her shawl, the tenderness of my movements belying the frank affability of my earlier

50

declaration. She seemed disconcerted. I rejoiced at having pronounced the word 'friendship.' If I managed to cling to it I would be able to maintain a salutary distance between us.

In the car, I adopted an almost intimate tone and suggested that she might like to take one last drink, and the smile I allowed to raise my lips seemed to betoken a change in the nature of my feelings for her. Confused but excited, she accepted.

I stopped in front of one of those Parisian night-owl grocer's and bought a bottle of champagne.

'Where to?' murmured Fanfan, not daring to articulate the implicit 'your place or mine?'

'To Vienna!' I answered.

'Vienna?'

'Well I went all the way to Chamonix just to pick you an edelweiss, didn't I? But I'll have to cover your eyes if I'm to drive you to Vienna.'

Fanfan laughed and happily joined in the fantasy. I knotted her shawl at the back of her neck and headed for the film studios at Boulogne, where they had the scenery for some historical epic written by my father and set in the Vienna of 1815.

In his concern for my future, my father had got me in with the studio caretaker so that this obliging person would let me in whenever I wanted. The idea was that I should get to know about film making with a view to carving out a career in the movies, just in case some unlikely eventuality came between me and a rapid rise to the French presidency or the throne of Europe. Ever since his victory over cancer Dad had been a man in a hurry: he had no patience with contingencies and considered that I had no more than ten years to find a niche between Charles de Gaulle and Julius Caesar or, if I so chose, to overshadow Chaplin.

And so, as I told you, I knew the caretaker, and this kindly fellow often allowed me to bring my girl of the moment for a night of silent magic on the studio sets. Of course, these adolescent girls who now basked in the sun of my memory were mere walk-ons in my emotional drama. It was Fanfan who held the stage.

On the way to Boulogne I relished the pleasure of being with this unpredictable young woman who so captivated my heart. I was delighted with the pictur-esque charm of our evening. I savoured the discovery that my constant stalling gave me the key to imperish-able passion. Now I had escaped the disorder of Verdelot and the moroseness of wedlock à la Chante-bise. Yes, the solution was a singular one and incompat-ible with common sense, but as a Crusoé I felt at ease with the bizarre.

Driving along I went over the details of the surprise I was about to spring on Fanfan, concluding that you can never overdo the imagination when it comes to planning your romantic moments. I freely admit that the heart was and still is my favourite organ. I have nothing against the brain, mind you, but I think that all too often we reason, when in fact we should let ourselves be guided by feeling. If we did, old age would bring fewer regrets.

The paradox of my situation made me smile. Here I was, a seeker of love without friendship – in a word, passion – acting as the apostle of male-female friend-ship. Of course, Fanfan was still blindfolded, and so she did not notice.

'Where are we going?' she asked.

'Through a forest,' I replied as we drove along the banks of the Seine.

'Are we going to take a plane?'

'Yes, from a small airfield. I've hired a tourist plane.'

'You're joking!'

'No! And don't take that blindfold off, otherwise the trip's cancelled.'

My forceful suggestion was enough to make her keep her shawl over her eyes. Ten minutes later I parked the car in front of the Studios de Boulogne and told her to wait for me. The caretaker's son was acting as night-watchman, and he slipped me the key to the sets.

I went back to get Fanfan.

'Everything's ready, you can get out now, the plane's waiting.'

Fanfan gave me her hand and let me guide her into the studios. She thought she was in the hangars of an aerodrome.

'Hey, careful, there's a propeller. Get your head down!' I warned with suitable conviction.

We came to a dressing room and I asked her to slip on a silk and velvet dress – a real princess number over the skin-tight one she already had on. She was surprised at having so much room around her and wanted to know why she had to go through this fitting session before take-off. I told her I wanted her to be ready to waltz the moment we landed. At the same time, trembling with the excitement of entering a magic tale, I was slipping on the uniform of an Austro-Hungarian officer of the 1815 vintage.

Nothing I know is more thrilling than closing the

53

distance between us and our childhood longings. As a young boy I was always bored by Cowboys and Indians. The only thing that excited me was love, and as soon as I reached the age of reason I was led by my heart. My only motive for attending school was the partiality I felt for this or that classmate, and if the playground proved barren of girls worthy of amatory interest I didn't turn up. While my friends threw themselves into sport and filled their Sundays with their hobbies, I ran after girls. Girls were my only escape route from reality.

I had always dreamed of being a Prince Charming in Hapsburg imperial uniform, and now here I was in the costume of my youthful dreams.

I led Fanfan onto the set and put a record of Viennese waltzes on the sound engineer's stereo system.

Then, with great emotion, I took a deep breath, stuck out my chest, and stepped up to her.

'Mademoiselle,' I said, 'would you honour me with a dance?'

Fanfan was still blindfolded.

'What's going on?' she said.

My heart aflame, I took her by the waist, whipped away the blindfold and started dancing. The moment she could see she flushed with surprise and exhilaration. There she was spinning around in my arms, her hips swathed in the blooming corolla of a princess gown, sweeping over the perfect reconstruction of a Viennese ballroom. There may have been lighting galleries and bridges for the boom man above all the wooden panelling and mirrors, but she was thrilled by the majesty and richness of this spacious setting. Suddenly, she found herself projected into the cinematic world she so cherished and had set her sights on conquering. She waltzed, radiant, weightless.

'Well, I did promise to take you to Vienna, didn't I?' I murmured.

Fanfan gave me an emotional hug. I was content. I could ask for nothing more than to make her happy. I wanted it to be like this for ever, but lust soon barged in when I felt her breasts brushing my body and her breath on my neck. I stood back slightly, but the precaution was useless. The demon of lechery continued to whisper in my ear thoughts that I tried not to hear. But try as I might my hands still felt and enjoyed the curve at the small of her back. Her silky suppleness urged me to let myself go. I did my best to think of something else, but I was incapable of distracting my desires and Fanfan was surely aware of her power over me. Her eyes glowed and she gave me a look so frank that it reached the depths of my soul. I had to look away.

I let go of her and stepped back, beating a strategic retreat from passion. The thought of the somnolent Chantebise couple was enough to silence any declarations. God knows, the so-called deliverance of the first kiss is a pure illusion, and the mornings after are full of headaches.

'Don't you want to dance any more?' The aplomb with which she said this was spiked with provocation.

'No, let's go out on to the terrace and drink the champagne before it gets warm,' I answered, offering my arm.

As she took it, she said something that went straight to my heart:

'Know you, sir, that last night Prince Metternich spoke most enthusiastically to me of your qualities? You are much in his mind for the embassy of London.'

Fanfan was playing the game. We continued with a discussion of the future of Europe after the havoc wrought by Napoleon and proceeded to a false terrace overlooking a giant model of Viennese rooftops. All around us were superb and odourless artificial bouquets. The waltzes played on in the background.

I poured Fanfan some champagne and leant lightly on the cork balustrade which, thanks to the excellent work of the painters, really did look like stone. Fanfan emptied her glass and threw it over her shoulder with a smile. The crystal shattered on the parquet.

'Well, we are in a film,' she said, as if to excuse herself.

Then, soft and low, she added, 'Tonight we can do anything we want.'

I was drunk with pleasure. I looked her right in the eyes, then followed up with a declaration of friendship. She was manifestly shaken. Though she tried to make a show of detachment, her disappointment was written all over her face.

'Isn't it wonderful,' I concluded brightly, 'you and I being so close, without so much as a shadow of ulterior motives?'

At this point I gave her a thorough briefing on my amorous past, playing on her emotions and all the while professing nothing but the purest, most unadulterated friendship. Fanfan was one of those beings with a special gift for pleasure and pain. She was finding it hard to breathe, and so was I. Her presence made me suffer and so did my own repressed passion, but at least my vanity was flattered by my display of willpower.

Now I wanted to awaken Fanfan's consoling instincts. I explained to her how terribly I had been wounded by the women I knew, and that I was still waiting for the relationship that would answer all my expectations. I confided my disappointment at the way girls resigned themselves to the decay of love. Then I sketched out the existence I imagined sharing with the girl of my heart. My words seemed to fill her soul with bitter regret. I was in seventh heaven.

When she had heard me out, poor wounded Fanfan made bold to reply:

'I can understand ... It's the same with me. I've never met anyone for whom love was the be all and end all.'

'Perhaps you have a friend who is as disillusioned as you are? You could introduce her to me. Unfortunately I can't think of anyone who might satisfy you.'

'Nor can I,' said Fanfan, trying to hide her disappointment.

I had just dealt the final blow. I hated having to do it but this was the only way I knew of keeping her. I did not want to lay my hands on her, but nor could I let her give herself to another man. She had to be branded.

Fanfan looked desolate in her princess's dress. Out of compassion, I took her hand to lead her away: 'Come ...'

We entered a forest of synthetic resin trees, penetrated another film, and ended up in the bedroom of a Venetian palace whose windows opened onto the Grand Canal.

'This is our room,' I murmured. 'We shall spend the

night here. We won't go back to Paris until tomorrow morning.'

For a moment, Fanfan was transfixed with astonishment. Then she smiled, as if everything she had heard up to now had been a misunderstanding. I quickly pointed out that my intentions were entirely honourable and above board.

'It's an old French custom, a way of learning restraint. Don't you know it? It was something they used to do in the country, the idea has always appealed to me.'

Then, with a laugh, I added, 'Don't worry, you can count on me to control myself.'

Fanfan forced out a soft little laugh as I stretched out on the bed in my Austrian officer's costume.

'Won't you join me?' I asked with a candour she took to be sincere.

She came and lay at my side. No doubt she thought this promiscuity would bring out the animal in me, but I maintained a nonchalance you would never associate with a man amorous or aroused. I forbade myself the slightest tremor of desire.

We returned to the subject of the singular intercourse that had developed between us since our first meeting. I kept shooting ambiguous glances at her and edging towards a confession of love by way of analogies and allusions, but never came out with the actual words. Having sufficiently raised her hopes, I proceeded to wreck them by uttering the word 'friendship'. This manoeuvre struck me as an excellent way of working Fanfan into a passion violent enough to be self-perpetuating. Her presence filled me with intense feelings, but I fought hard to remain lucid, struggling to resist the amatory trance that was beginning to come over me.

I hinted at my desire to see her behave as a true friend, making it understood that by reining in our physical desire we would be forging an indissoluble bond. We could never leave each other because we would not be 'together'.

As I spoke the lines on her forehead told me she rejected my ideas. The mercurial play of her changing expressions was stunning. I could see her passion grow with each new denial.

You will probably be amazed to hear that my will was not swept away the moment Fanfan lay down on the bed – Fanfan who promised such pleasure, whose burning eyes bespoke such desire, such expectation; Fanfan, whom I knew to be the love of my life, the one without whom I would never really be myself. Well, for a start I did derive intense pleasure from leading Fanfan into the fiery heart of lust. But, on the other hand, betraying Laure would also have required an awesome amount of courage. The mere thought of Verdelot was enough to make me tremble in my adulterous boots.

No one else can understand this. To do so, they would need to have experienced the amorous mayhem which held sway behind the gaping silences and super-ficial gaiety of my mother's house.

Besides, I was confused. I still loved Laure and Fanfan worried me as much as she attracted me. I resented her threat to my reasonable and reassuring existence with Laure.

Yet for all that I was just as readily stirred by the sight of Fanfan's superb beauty. My effort to pre-empt the mutiny of my instincts took the form of concentrating

on a train travelling at high speed through the country-
side. Banishing all other thoughts, I mentally conjured
up a locomotive, every nut and bolt of it.

And that is how I managed to loosen the grip of my
desire.

I preferred the anticipation of Fanfan's caresses to
kissing and cuddling in the present. I trusted in the
powerful effects of anticipation. I was certain that it
would make us the first couple to enjoy a full half
century of passionate love, uncorrupted by humdrum
compromises.

I grant that my methods may appear austere, or even
tough, but I was acting in Fanfan's best interests as well
as my own. The incredible tension between us was a
source of pleasure for her too, and pleasure of the
keenest kind.

I slipped away from the palace bedroom before Fanfan
could wake up. I wanted her to remember her Viennese
evening as a kind of dream, and that meant the prince
had to vanish overnight.

I took off my costume and went out to clear my head
with a couple of coffees in a bar. Outside, spring was
going through the motions. The day was dawning for all
and sundry, but especially for me, the happy victor in
my battle against sensuality.

In my ears I could still hear the echo of the locomotive I had forced myself to concentrate on until sleep
came. During that night of self-control my lust had
become so acute it was more than flesh and blood could
bear – and yet I had held out. My joy was mingled with
a feeling of heroism.

That day was twelve hours of exquisite happiness. I smiled, life smiled on me. I gave up my seat on the métro with alacrity; I was thanked. I was in love and felt I had it in me to safeguard my passion against the ravages of time. I had been strong enough to suspend my desire for a whole night; surely I had the strength to do so for life.

That evening I was back with Laure. She cooed in my arms and reminded me that Sunday was 'cleaning day'. I clammed up. And while I was hoovering she narrated the deeds and words of the Chantebise family: or, to put it more plainly, she paraphrased what she had already told me a good thirty times before. The Chantebise clan stuck doggedly to the same old Sunday routine: boring breakfast, Mass observed with sheep-like devotion, lunch with 'Madame de Chantebise Senior' – as venomous as ever – cards and other games at three and, finally, the compulsory collective promenade. Enough to shoot down my remaining high spirits.

We dined in front of the TV. There was a film Laure wanted to watch. My heavy body sagged with sadness as if, twenty years before my time, I had slipped into her parents' shapeless clothes.

During a commercial break she looked at me and asked, 'Have you found some work experience for Sciences-Po?'

'No.'

'It's important for your CV, you know. If you like my parents could help you get something with LMO Dublanc, the boiler people. Come to think of it, it wouldn't be bad if you could get a job with them afterwards, would it?'

My curriculum vitae, a boiler company, Sciences-Po ... it was all so far away from me, from Fanfan's madcap, passionate existence. Had I really been put on the terrestrial crust to sell boilers? My delicious friend Laure suddenly made me want very much to vomit.

Next we began negotiations concerning our marriage. Laure refused to compromise. I raised my voice. A row ensued.

Laure wanted to order the mawkish and idiotic type of wedding invitations hallowed by tradition. Worse still, she wanted to invite the whole herd of Chantebises to our nuptials, and to compile a wedding list containing only items of crockery from some refined rip-off merchant who had already supplied seven generations of her family. My sadness turned to irritation. She also wanted me to go through the great day dressed in tails, like an undertaker. My irritation turned to animosity.

I could sense the sinister significance of the approaching conflict. If I capitulated now, I might just as well give up any hope of running my own life. The slightest sign of uxoriousness and Laure would feel free to tighten her grip on our life together. The next thing I knew I'd be having to accept the hideous carpets her mother would certainly foist on us. And that was only the beginning. Therefore I refused to comply.

Just before bed, Laure went to the toilet adjoining our bedroom and urinated noisily with the door open. Then, quite without shame, she farted. Now that we had set the date of our wedding, she was getting a little careless. Sometimes she burped right in my face. 'I've got wind in my tummy,' she said.

This time I had no need to concentrate on locomotives

to keep myself from touching my bedfellow. 'A couple': how sickening that term now sounded to me. The thought of having to hit the sack with Laure for the next half century was truly chilling.

My chaste romance with Fanfan now made the laxity I could once tolerate unbearable. How absurd it seemed to remain faithful just to break with the mores of Verdelot and protect myself from the passion inspired by Fanfan. Had my will alone not been strong enough to overcome my desire the previous night? The image of Laure and the awareness of being bound to her had been no help whatsoever.

But did I have the guts to break free? That was the agonizing question. The idea of reproducing my parents' own failure was deeply upsetting to me: I had such high hopes of escaping the sad fate that dogs so many modern love affairs.

Laure made an attempt to snuggle up to me. How poor this contact was after the light, feathery touches in which I had so intensely felt the soft sweetness of Fanfan's flesh.

So, was I to quit Laure without further ado or grant our relationship a reprieve?

Coward that I was, I fell asleep on the question.

SIX

LEAVING HOME THE NEXT MORNING I CAME FACE TO
face on the landing with a blond man who had just
emerged from my mother's flat.

I had seen him several times before at her dinner
parties. She had introduced him as 'a friend'. I caught
him staring at her. His manner – the reporter used to
surprises ('I am paid to exercise my curiosity' he said one
evening) – made a favourable first impression. He
looked a youthful forty and there were times when the
Protestant reserve of his expression melted in the heat of
intense enthusiasm.

Seeing me, he became embarrassed and inhibited. I
returned his greeting as if washing my hands of an
obligation. We got into the lift.

The silence lasted until the ground floor.

In the course of this vertical voyage my feelings about

Laure executed a quick volte face. This reminder of
Verdelot had shaken me to the bones – yet another
emotional earthquake. Suddenly I was back to dreaming
of a stable, immutable marriage. I forgave Laure for
belonging to the Chantebise clan, for her boilers, her
domestic tyranny and her flatulence.

By the time the lift had stopped, my decision was
made. I would agree to her ridiculous invitations. It
didn't even matter if she dug up her whole family tree
for the wedding.

After all, Laure was a charming girl and she wasn't
the only one to blame for the degradation of our love.
Yes, there were evenings when I behaved like a typical
husband. There were times when I was deaf to what she
was telling me, when I forgot to put a little feeling into
our life together.

And yet I still hoped with all my heart that one day I
would experience sublime and idyllic romance. I still
wanted to remain Prince Charming to my elected love
until death carried me away.

The only solution was to keep my distance from
Fanfan. That way at least her image of me would be in
harmony with the romantic ideal I aspired to. I had to
know there was a woman somewhere who would always
think of me as a perfect and perennially seductive lover.

And then, to tell the truth, I was more than a little
reluctant to get involved in Fanfan's life. Laure made no
demands on me, it was enough that I should pursue my
studies at Sciences-Po and sell boilers until retirement,
that I should not forget to make conscientious love to
her (provided we stuck to the missionary position and
used a bed); she would be satisfied with my services.

Fanfan, on the other hand, would set me face to face with my destiny. Of course, she was much too subtle to force me into anything, but she would be sure to remind me of my birthright: I was Alexander Crusoé, not Alexander the Insignificant. After all, she was actively pursuing her own dreams. She wouldn't understand if I shied away from mine.

Now as a matter of fact I found my secret aspirations rather worrying. I had always wanted to improve upon the reality I considered intolerable by writing for the theatre. Once, in secret, I tried to write a play. I would have been as ashamed as a virgin caught masturbating if anyone had found out. So, when I had written the last scene of the first version, I panicked and burnt the whole lot. It would all have turned out differently if my father's cancer had proved fatal, but there he still was, striking dread into my soul with the example of his life as a writer before me. The way he needed to spread chaos all around in his quest for the Absolute terrified me. I had no desire whatsoever to follow in his footsteps. I was afraid that if I let my pen wander over the white paper it would lead me to my childhood fears. Laure certainly did nothing to activate the playwright vegetating within me. She preferred to see me on the payroll of the boiler manufacturers. She may not have had the magnetism of Fanfan's free spirit, but in her arms I did at least feel safe.

My decision to remain faithful to her was confirmed not long after the chance meeting in the lift. That same day I had lunch with my father, and he came out with this gem of a witticism:

'If ever you become a writer, try to have several

mistresses. That gives you a greater chance of being abandoned, and therefore more opportunities to experience suffering.'

I knew then that I would never write. That I would be an eternal monogamist.

A few days later, in my father's sitting room, Fanfan showed two of her films in the presence of a producer by the name of Gabilan.

Gabilan had accumulated a sufficient number of debts for the banks to take him seriously. Every so often he would spread the rumour that he was planning to emigrate to Italy. Put on the alert, the bankers crowded into his office with offers of extra capital to keep him working in France, in the hope of clawing back a bit of money. With Gabilan in Italy, they knew they could kiss their centimes goodbye.

If, by some freak of cinema, one of Gabilan's films failed to lose money, and the distributor paid him a nice little cheque, Gabilan would negotiate this sum with each of his bankers. The winner was the one who gave the most favourable rescheduling conditions for his debt. As for the others, their punishment and fall from favour was signified by six months without a dinner invitation.

Gabilan was a naturally contented sort of person, enveloped in fat and blithely indifferent to his financial difficulties. For him, cinema was a dream and bankers were duty-bound to provide generous or even ruinous support.

Gabilan was much taken with Fanfan's temperament. Moreover, he claimed to be dazzled by her Super 8 films – the Western and a fantasy. I assumed he meant it, for Gabilan never lied unless he had to. Besides, his compliments were accompanied by an offer that had Fanfan reeling with happiness.

'You can be second assistant on my next two films, and assistant director on the one after those. I want you to get used to handling a real crew. After that I'll see about producing your first film in 35mm. What do you say?'

Fanfan threw her arms round him and kissed him on the cheeks. Gabilan didn't know what to do with himself.

My father was dazzled too, but by Fanfan's stunning beauty. I really didn't like the little flame that flickered in his eyes when he looked at her. I found his praise suspect. Gabilan's wasn't – his only known emotional life was his passionate relationship with venomous reptiles. The great love of his life went by the name of Marcel, and was a cobra over five metres long.

The moment Gabilan had gone Dad turned his charm on Fanfan as though I simply wasn't there. He was funny, extravagant and witty. In a matter of seconds you found yourself wanting to please him. Fanfan was fascinated. They were kindred souls. Cinema people. Both had the courage to leave their fears behind them. I panicked and, taking Fanfan by the arm, dragged her away from my father's blandishments.

In the street, Fanfan at last gave voice to her joy. Gabilan had fulfilled her dearest hopes. The next fifteen minutes were one long sequence of exultant whooping, exclamations of pleasure, anticipatory trips to a cloud-free future, and statements of gratitude to destiny, myself and life.

Afterwards we strolled our way through a string of chic boutiques and lavish stores, acting as if our funds were as unlimited as our desires. My bank account was only modestly stocked and Fanfan's had long been a trampoline for cheques, but that didn't stop us acting rich and choosing clothes that only imagination could add to our wardrobes.

Fanfan was amazed to see me enjoying it all so much. There are not many men who allow themselves to be dragged around the shops with such good grace. I didn't dare tell her that my raptures were inspired not by the articles displayed in the shop windows but by the reflection of her body. Likewise, it was her figure that sent me into ecstasy, not, as I pretended, the cut of the dress she was trying.

We took the métro to get to some more of her favourite shops. Luckily, the trains were bursting and in the crush of our fellow passengers I was able to squeeze up against her and enjoy the exquisite firmness of her breasts. I had to bite my lips to stop myself kissing her and thrust my hands in my pockets before they could get out of control. Fanfan had had enough of standing, so she leaned over to a man who was sitting: 'If you gave me your seat,' she said sweetly, 'I'd really be very happy. I am so tired.'

The man was touched and vacated his flip-up perch. Fanfan smiled. 'Thank you so much.'

She had a knack for making things easy, did Fanfan. She had none of the apprehensions which inhibit most human beings. I was fascinated by the way she allowed herself such freedom.

This was the moment I chose to mention Laure,

whom I said I had just met and wouldn't be forgetting in a hurry. My voice quavered with fictitious emotion. 'At last, I think I've found a girl who shares my dreams.'

Of course I didn't tell her that Laure was my mistress. The simple possibility was enough to unsettle her. This was perfect. But to spare Fanfan any unnecessary pain, I added in an offhand sort of way that I wondered if this Laure would make a worthwhile conquest. Her face brightened immediately.

After our métro journey Fanfan took me into a lingerie shop. Then, as if to obliterate the image of Laure, she tried on all the underwear likely to arouse me, walking to and fro in front of me like an angel oblivious to the power of her charms. Once again I had to rely on that trusty steam locomotive from our Viennese evening to keep me from fainting with desire. When Fanfan spoke to me, I tried to cover her words with the noise of the wheels. The salesgirls thought we were lovers. Fanfan was delighted and I was choking with lust.

I spluttered something about a fictive lecture at Sciences-Po and ran off before my will gave way. Fanfan watched me go with an expression of smug incredulity on her face, in her eyes, and in her every feature. How could anyone resist this display of her charms? I suppose she resented it. And I don't doubt that her subsequent perseverance in the task of seducing me was motivated in part by a desire for revenge.

Outside, alone in the street, I felt strangely uneasy. The reason slowly dawned on me. The afternoon had gone like a dream. We had played at being rich and had remained unreal. Now I wanted more than anything to smash that glass screen between me and my dreams, to bring them into my biography. Being a film-set prince wasn't good enough any more. I craved the exhilaration I had experienced when I set off to pick an edelweiss in the Alps. Fanfan had won me over to her point of view: 'positive is the only way to think'.

The upshot of these reflections was that I now retraced my footsteps, revisiting every boutique and buying up the blouses, dresses and linen trousers she had taken a fancy to, blissfully consigning myself deep into overdraft. Escaping from reality was amazingly simple. Tomorrow, trouble might call, but for the moment I felt free, borne along by my own daring, happy to exist. I was a new man. What had become of the sensible, moderate student from Sciences-Po? Through the cracks in my conformism emerged the passionate and pushy persona I had always found so worrying.

I deposited my two huge bags of purchases 'for Mademoiselle Sauvage' with Fanfan's concierge then slipped away. I was jubilant at the thought that, for Fanfan, the contents of these plastic bags would be tangible proof of my power to convert the wildest desires into reality. I had just complicated my life with thirty-two thousand three hundred francs' worth of debt. It is a sum I shall remember for many years to come, but at the time it seemed purely abstract.

Having taken care to buy duplicates of each ravishing item of underwear, that evening I asked Laure to slip on the ones I had kept. My hope was that the lingerie would create for me the illusion of sleeping with Fanfan. Laure was touched and complied willingly with my request. She thought the gift was a homage to the beauty of her body, and it is true that she had a pretty good one. But her complexion couldn't compare with Fanfan's.

That night Laure was unusually bold. I was happy, but her caresses seemed so much less exquisite than the ones Fanfan could have lavished on me.

The next day I received a telegram from Fanfan: *You forgot the little white suit – Stop – Friendly? greetings – Stop – Fanfan.*

This oversight notwithstanding, I now faced a serious cash-flow crisis. I therefore hurried out to request a student loan from my banker. This affable stuffed-suit simply straightened his tie and opened the valves of credit. I had two years in which to pay – up to the end of my studies – but he made it clear that his generosity would go no further.

Then he added, 'I must say I'm rather surprised by this sudden expenditure. Thirty-two thousand three hundred francs, all in one go. You were always so reasonable. What happened?'

'Tell me, have you ever been in love, really head over heels?'

And that was the end of our discussion. My banker had no way of accounting for passion.

I had just indebted myself for the years ahead. Yet I was proud of the fact: I had acquired this burden for love, and that's a lot better than a washing machine.

I pushed on to my father's house to collect his car registration book. He had had it made out with my name and address – not because he wanted to give me the car, but to make sure the fines I so eagerly incurred when I borrowed it would know where to roost. Of course, I never paid them. Irresponsible driving was my way of punishing him for exasperating me. Whenever I saw him arm in arm with some new mistress I took his car and parked it in a pedestrian area. Two hundred and thirty francs was the sting usually attached. At first he tried to make me cough up but I simply played for time until the bailiffs came knocking on his door. Thus he generally ended up paying these – as I saw it – well-deserved fines. He also tried to stop me using his car but I had a copy of the key which somehow I could never find when he barked for it. Ever since I had started carrying out these reprisals, my father – who hadn't a clue as to their cause – had become extremely cheesed off with me.

Anatole was in the flat when I arrived. He informed me that Daddy was playing in the bath with his mask and snorkel. He was waiting for him.

I found Anatole de Machecourt awesome and terrifying, and both to equal extremes. His friends called him Titanic. He had spent twenty years in close communion with heroin, and yet he had never hit the bottom. People said he was unsinkable, just like the ship.

With his feral physique and tormented soul, Titanic was strikingly dissimilar from your common or garden human being. He was a man of Herculean vices and epic wickedness. He gleefully assumed that all men are ripe for evil, and worked indefatigably for the perversion of souls. That, quite simply, was the way he was made. He got his kicks from luring loving wives off the straight and narrow and into his bed. Nuns, he believed, were simply prostitutes who had yet to discover their true vocation, and deserved a little career guidance. If he saw an old lady giving sweets to a child his first thought was 'poison!' and a strange light came into his eyes whenever he stroked a dog. Later I was to find out that his sex life had as few limits as his imagination. No domain of the animal kingdom was beneath him – or rather they all were: women, men, tortoises and various small mammals, such was his ordinary fare, and he never failed to try out a new temptation. On one occasion I saw him making a pass at an octogenarian former prime minister: the man went so pale we thought his bell had tolled.

Words became twisted in Titanic's mouth. Love meant lying, kissing signified betrayal, to pay a compliment was synonymous with fawning and to use implied to abuse. The only true things about him were his falseness and his sublime friendship for my father – his one spot of purity.

I suppose Dad must have been touched by Titanic's veneration for him, and I am sure he too was fascinated by this demon who knew Tolstoy by heart and whose memory ranged at ease among all the greatest authors. Titanic could drone out cantos from the *Divine Comedy* for hours on end.

Titanic was a tireless polygraph who exercised his talents in three separate spheres. For one thing he wrote novels in a dazzling, luxuriant style, stretching beyond dictionary French to neologisms he coined from Latin and ancient Greek, languages he spoke almost fluently. He also wrote articles for a popular magazine in classically perfect French. And finally, it was Titanic who crafted the so-called readers' confessions for a pornographic magazine – not to mention the hair-raising advice proffered by the in-house 'sexologist'.

All of which would have been very quaint if he had been inoffensive, but our eloquent friend Titanic was not innocuous. Not that he ever forced anyone to do anything. His favourite method was to outflank his victims, seducing them with his illusorily attractive personality and sumptuous language the better to exert his nefarious influence. With Titanic around you started to think terrible thoughts. You spoke words you would never have uttered in any other circumstances. Titanic stirred the murkiness of latent evil and weakened people's consciences, encouraging their cowardice or treachery. And he was all the more dangerous because he took you by surprise, appearing just when you were ripe for him. After that he wouldn't let you out of his iron grip till he knew you were ready to roll down the slippery slope.

That night he must have sensed I was hard up because he jokingly told me that, with the logbook in my name, I could always pawn the car if I needed a little cash. I refused to answer.

I kissed my father, took the logbook from his desk and ran off, trying to forget Titanic's insidious and odious suggestion.

SEVEN

THE IMAGE OF FANFAN HAUNTED ME LIKE A REFRAIN.
For a while, I felt the fever of those who burn for the
crowning consummation of a kiss. The very fibres of my
being seemed to slacken as if to accommodate this
delightful and self-induced feeling of expectancy.

What I aspired to was not love and its reciprocal
display of tender solicitude, but the headlong excitement which sweeps away routine, blasts out boredom
and gives spice to existence; for the first time, I had the
feeling that my passion would go on for ever.

Little by little, my precariously balanced and overwrought emotions were toppling into chaos.

Fanfan may have occupied my every thought, but I
was still sharing a bed with Laure. Soon I found I
couldn't even look her in the eye. My character was
buckling under the weight of my clandestine emotions.

The certainty that I was at fault brought me out in violent palpitations. And yet, by some strange trick of my mind, this was the moment I chose to start making all sorts of plans with Laure, as if these could redeem my feelings for Fanfan, as if by filling our future I could convince myself that we did indeed have one. Nevertheless my secret was becoming more unbearable by the day. It felt like living a lie.

Worse, my senses were inflamed, and the fire soon spread beyond my control. I was in a kind of stupor, the victim of an imperious and mind-numbing desire, lost for whole afternoons at a time in the delectation of chimerical delights. I grew languid. I became listless. I saw myself spending the night in intense discussions with Fanfan, revealing the Alexandre I hid from Laure. I was being ground down by my hunger for perpetually postponed pleasures.

I began to lose my common sense. I neglected to feed myself, to sleep, or even to feign an interest in my daily life. I kept losing my keys and on one occasion left the same café twice without paying the bill. If by some chance I failed to miss a meeting completely I was always astonishingly late. My studies were drifting gently out of control, and the few classes I attended were no more than a chance to indulge in my dreams of living with Fanfan as a spontaneous young man, liberated at last from my childhood. My all-consuming agitation over-whelmed my feeble attempts to keep up with the teacher. I was the ghost of the shadow of the reasonable, punc-tual and assiduous student I had once been. Sometimes I wondered how I could have changed so much in so short a time.

Laure found my state extremely worrying and sent me to have my body looked at by a doctor. Good salesman that he was, the fellow naturally discovered an illness. Laure was reassured and could now wait for the prescribed treatment to make me better.

I was unable either to love Fanfan or to speak about her. Confiding in a friend would have been too painful. Even though my infidelity to Laure was only mental, someone else's knowledge of it would somehow bring me closer to the self-image from which I was struggling to break free.

I began to doubt the soundness of my resolution. Why not simply decide to take Fanfan in my arms and get it over with? One thing was clear: I couldn't go on carrying the burden of my overwrought and undirected emotions. And yet, however intense, this feeling of deprivation was itself a constant source of pleasure. I could not bring myself to break off this amatory foreplay.

Literature, theatre and film all taught me that however much excitement may survive the first kiss, it is only a pale copy of the exhilaration that lies in anticipating love. When authors and script writers invent obstacles in their emotional life it is only to take their minds off the bitter truth: when hope is dead then passion is moribund. Besides, my past torment justified the torments to come. I refused to admit that I had suffered in vain.

No, the best thing was to temper my lust. Not that I wanted to become indifferent towards Fanfan, but I did want to be rid of my debilitating excess desire. To this end I had the idea of jotting down in a notebook the dreams that crowded my mind, along with scenes from my imaginary life with Fanfan. After that I tried to soothe the irritation of my senses with the analgesic effects of masturbation. But while this method did afford brief lulls, my attempts ended in failure and my loins only flared up anew. What I needed was to be caressed by Fanfan's gentle gaze.

I had given up all hope of controlling my passions when, one day, having drifted into a class at Sciences-Po, I found myself listening to a professor of marketing:

'Pavlov's experiments with dogs demonstrated the existence of conditioned reflexes which can be used in advertising. He observed that if you ring a bell when you feed a dog, once the dog has been conditioned, you only need to ring a bell for the creature to salivate. You no longer need to give him food to stimulate his saliva glands.'

Inspired by this striking discovery, I decided at once to 'condition' myself. My aim, however, was the opposite of Pavlov's. I wanted not to salivate when I imagined the charming Fanfan. I would therefore have to substitute some unpleasant sensation for the bell.

The torments of passion can drive a man to wild ideas.

I hurried home in a state of joyous expectation, then went straight down to the cellar and stood my mother's bicycle on its saddle. I stripped the dynamo wires, stuck them under my fingers and waited for the radiant image of Fanfan to float into my mind. The moment it appeared, I kicked the peddles round and gave myself a mild electric shock. (Putting my fingers in the socket struck me as a little bit excessive). I had repeated this operation ten times or more, screaming on each occasion, when the door swung open to reveal the concierge's blankly uncomprehending face. He must have heard my yelps.

'What are you doing, Monsieur Crusoé?' His accent carried a whiff of old Algeria.

This was embarrassing. I removed the wires from under my fingernails and told him all about the difficulties of repairing bicycles. He looked at me strangely.

I never did find out whether conditioning can remedy the ravages of passion; but I am sure that my feelings were too violent for one such as Pavlov to control.

Fanfan had me under her spell.

Sometimes I thought, 'So why don't you and Fanfan have a quick, secret fling?'

After all, that's how most husbands ease their desires, isn't it? Such interludes rarely topple the conjugal regime. The adulterers end up working out some kind of compromise with their conscience, and thus manage to steal a little pleasure from life before old age catches up with them.

What wouldn't I have given to be so easygoing!

But becoming a lover would plunge me into the nightmare world of Verdelot. The mere thought of transgression made me break out in a cold sweat.

Quite simply, I am incapable of loving by halves. I envy men who can kiss a girl without making any promises, people for whom love is just a delightful sport. I often dream of such frivolity. My gravity is a millstone around my neck. I must get it from my parents. Their polygamy was never light-hearted. As for me, the idea of eternity has always been an essential ingredient of my emotions.

The idea of bedding Fanfan one evening and giving her notice the morning after – or even a few days later – was simply unthinkable. This, after all, was Fanfan. Perhaps I could have had a one-night stand with someone else, but Fanfan was no casual acquaintance. Fanfan was the woman I was born to love.

I knew in my bones that our relationship would mean the end for me and Laure, that it would ineluctably lead to our living together. Given that only the enchantment of budding passion was good enough for Fanfan and myself, such a conclusion would be far too dangerous.

Of course, I could always leave Fanfan as soon as the intensity of our romance showed signs of waning, but I adored her too much to disabuse her so brutally. It would have been a crime to commit myself, in the certain knowledge that sooner or later I would be forced to break off in order to protect our relationship from the corroding effects of time.

And then, as I have said, I found Fanfan's freedom of spirit disconcerting. With her I knew I would have no choice but to write.

Laure had gone to spend the weekend with her parents.

I succumbed to necessity and arranged for Fanfan to come round at six o'clock on Saturday evening. I said I needed her to help me rehearse a play I was performing in June with the Sciences-Po drama group. I was too full of her to bear her absence for long, but I was also confident of my ability to smother desire in its cradle. That, at least, is how I felt. Had I not already proved it by preventing the love in my heart from rising to my lips?

I didn't know it, but I was overestimating my strength of will.

All that mattered now was my lust for life. I was sick of depriving myself. The desire to see her overwhelmed any feelings of guilt.

By six o'clock on Saturday, I had removed every trace of Laure's belongings. When Fanfan came in, my feelings stood firm. My breathing remained steady. I could control my senses without doing violence to myself.

Having poured her a cup of tea, I asked her to get up on a stool and become Juliet, for the scene where Romeo has climbed into Capulet's orchard and is speaking to Juliet from below her window. Then I handed her a copy of the play.

Of course, I had no intention whatsoever of putting on *Romeo and Juliet* with my fellow students at Sciences-Po, but the exercise was far from gratuitous. For just one evening, I wanted to borrow from Shakespeare the words of love that Fanfan and I would never be able to exchange.

Fanfan pretended not to understand.

I explained that it was the part of the play where Romeo has hidden below Juliet's window one night and heard her declaiming her passion for him, that after a while it has become too much to bear and he has decided to show himself. I told her she should feel free to correct my diction and intonation, but didn't reveal that Juliet says a lot more in this scene than Romeo.

I went up to Fanfan and looked her passionately in the eyes. Not a difficult thing to do. Standing on her stool with the text in her hand, she began:

'By whose direction found'st thou out this place?'
'By Love, that first did prompt me to inquire;
He lent me counsel, and I lent him eyes.'
I was overjoyed. As I spoke, her features replied in the unmistakable language of passion. Shakespeare's poetry was doing its work.
She continued:
'Thou know'st the mask of night is on my face,
Else would a maiden blush bepaint my cheek
For that which thou hast heard me speak to-night.
Fain would I dwell on form, fain, fain deny
What I have spoke: but farewell compliment!
Dost thou love me? I know thou wilt say 'Ay',
And I will take thy word; yet if thou swear'st,
Thou may'st prove false; at lovers' perjuries,
They say, Jove laughs. O gentle Romeo,
If thou dost love, pronounce it faithfully:
Or if thou think'st I am too quickly won,
I'll frown and be perverse and say thee nay,
So thou wilt woo; but else, not for the world.
In truth, fair Montague, I am too fond,
And therefore thou may'st think my 'haviour light:
But trust me, gentleman, I'll prove more true
Than those that have more cunning to be strange.
I should have been more strange, I must confess,
But that thou overheard'st, ere I was ware,
My true love's passion: therefore pardon me,
And not impute this yielding to light love,
Which the dark night hath so discovered.'

By now, Fanfan and I were struggling in a maelstrom of passion. At any moment we would be swept away. Yet I continued, in the hope that as long as my lips were articulating words they would be unable to seek out Fanfan's. With each line of verse, our need to kiss grew more agonizing.

She was trembling.

'Good night, good night! as sweet repose and rest
Come to thy heart as that within my breast!'

My answer was just as sincere:

'O! wilt thou leave me so unsatisfied?'

'What satisfaction canst thou have tonight?'

'The exchange of thy love's faithful vow for mine.'

Upon which I put my hand on hers.

She shuddered. Our bodies were begging for the release of an embrace; but Fanfan found it within herself and Shakespeare's verse to delay the moment still further:

'I gave thee mine before thou didst request it;
And yet I would it were to give again.'

'Wouldst thou withdraw it? for what purpose, love?'

'But to be frank, and give it thee again.'

This last line opened the floodgates. I couldn't wait a moment longer. I had to say something. My emotion was in full spate. I spoke with a passion that made her tremble.

'Fanfan!'

But before I could go on the door was thrown open and there was Laure, looking utterly disconsolate. I panicked.

'Fanfan, have I got the tone right? Oh . . . Laure, it's you!'

'Hello,' said Fanfan, her voice suddenly ice-cold.

'Fanfan, this is Laure, my fiancée and flatmate. Laure,

Fanfan, a director friend who was kind enough to help
me rehearse.'

'Oh. I didn't know you were in a play.'

This was not very helpful of Laure.

'Well I am. I've just joined a theatre group at
Sciences-Po.'

The odds were hardly in my favour, but I decided to
act the innocent. Not only did I refuse to try and justify
this equivocal situation, but I even asked Laure to give
us more time. 'We've got about half an hour to go
before we finish. Would you mind waiting for me in a
café?'

Half an hour was all I needed to ask Fanfan's hand in
marriage and explain that Laure was no more than a
memory to me, an unfortunate misunderstanding. I was
tired of constantly having to resist my desire for Fanfan,
of forever deferring the ecstasies of physical passion, of
censoring the bold thoughts that assailed my brain
whenever I saw her, of living with her in mind but not in
body. Why not abandon my resolution there and then?
Nowadays, when everyone is led by their senses, the
promptings of the body are almost impossible to ignore.
So why try? She would make me fall in love with reality,
oblige me to become my true self. I wanted to share her
world, to weary her with love until death do us part.
And I wanted to sleep with her. Besides, it was cruel to
go on tormenting the girl.

But Laure refused to budge. 'I've something
important to tell you,' she declared. She looked quite
serious.

Fanfan was mortified by this sudden interruption.
Before I could react she was out of the door. She had a

meeting, she said. I was alone with Laure, who suddenly burst into tears. She sobbed out the news that her parents would be divorcing as soon as legally possible. That morning she had arrived in the middle of a family earthquake. Her mother had just found out that her husband, the insignificant Monsieur de Chantebise, had spent the last six years having weekly orgasms in another woman. Moreover, her rival did not even shave her armpits. 'I expect that whore's got hair under her arms as well!' she had said disdainfully. 'Yes, she has,' replied the unfaithful one.

Madame de Chantebise immediately demanded that their bodies and goods be separated.

'I think Mummy's going much too far,' said Laure. 'After all, it's her fault if Daddy decided to go elsewhere.'

'Yes, and that's exactly why she won't forgive him.'

Since Monsieur de Chantebise was in the habit of obeying the diktats of his spouse, he had agreed to move out of the conjugal home. That was why Laure had left earlier than expected.

All this came as a great shock to me. The Chantebises were one of the best-preserved couples I knew. They had lived together for twenty-five years and still didn't hate each other. Sometimes, in fact, they conversed and, amazingly enough, they never failed to nod each other a greeting in the morning. Chantebise still noticed when his wife wore a new frock, and his wife lavished all her tenderness on him. She even kissed his forehead in celebration of his name day.

This marital debacle taught me that the durability of love is an illusion. No one, it seemed, could escape the fatal decline of passion's first enchantments. Habit will make adulterers of us all. Laure might criticize her mother, but it was a fact that I found her less fetching than when we started going out. We imagine ourselves to be rich with some radiant future, and the word 'always' is always superfluous.

This new shock galvanized me into renewing my resolution: not to lay a finger on Fanfan, and thus to keep our passion away from the pitfalls of conjugal monotony. I would stick with the exquisite unhappiness of the languishing lover. Love's flower was so much finer than its fleshy fruit. This approach would fulfil all the dreams and appease all the fears in my agitated heart. The only way forward was to cultivate non-fulfilment. Of course, it would have been nice to think that my personal merits were enough to make her happy, but I saw no other way of satisfying Fanfan than keeping her dangling and hoping, in the fires of passion.

I thanked my lucky stars that Laure had arrived when she did. A few moments later, and the damage would have been done. I would have kissed Fanfan, thus ushering in the long, slow decline of our love. The fleeting vision of these consequences was frightening. My desire for stability reawoke. And when Laure sobbed and murmured, 'And then when I get home there's this girl here. It's really not my day,' I was well equipped to reassure her.

I spent the evening untangling her torment of doubts and discussing our rapidly approaching wedding. I reassured her, appeased her, and embroidered on reality. But I didn't lie. I really did want to be her faithful husband – physically at least. I was hoping that matrimony would save me from my instincts.

I knew perfectly well that my marriage would grow arid, that it would end up a desert. And that was precisely why the woman I wanted to marry could not be the love of my life.

Now there was nothing cynical about this. On the contrary, far from resigning myself to the decay of love, I had resolved to create a situation where at least one passion – mine, for Fanfan – could be saved from the flood. Poor Laure: I did love her, once, and I am deeply grateful to her for soothing the desires aroused by Fanfan. Without her help, I could never have fought off the tempter within.

EIGHT

ONE NIGHT I CAME HOME TO FIND THE FLAT IN TOTAL darkness. Laure must have gone out, I thought, or perhaps she simply wasn't home yet. Then I heard the clink of ice cubes knocking together in a glass. A lighter flashed on and a candle flame bloomed, revealing a gorgeously dressed and typically Latin temptress with bejewelled ears. My eyes were drawn to her deliciously pert breasts as they rose and fell to the rhythm of her breathing. She was sitting at a table set splendidly for two.

'*Ciao bambino!*' She greeted me in a suave, purring voice, then emptied her glass.

Lost for words I turned on the light. What I saw stunned me. Yes, I recognized the mischievous smile on that face. Then she burst into a peal of laughter. Laure!

Her light chestnut hair had disappeared under a black

wig. She had darkened her skin by the subtle use of make-up. She spoke with a light Italian accent, gesticulating to emphasize her words. The illusion was complete. She would have been perfectly at home in a crowd of Milanese, this 'Laura' – or 'Laora' as she now pronounced her name.

Our dinner was an exquisite moment of intimacy, rocked gently by slow Italian ballads delivered in those special husky voices to be found only on the other side of the Alps. It was all very touching, this attempt to entice me by a change of persona. She knew of my taste for artifice and was sure this would please me. At last, I thought, she had understood that although such surprises are insufficient in themselves, love cannot endure without them.

I assumed Laure had been needled by her chance meeting with Fanfan a few days earlier and that it had pushed her into taking this initiative. However much I denied it, she realized that Fanfan's beauty was much too spectacular for me not to desire her. Moreover, her parents' recent separation must have stung her into taking special care of our love, so as to save it and us from the same sorry fate.

I revelled in our gallant intercourse, happy in my heart to know that Laure was giving me free rein to flirt with this Italian and at the same time keeping me safe from the unfaithful Alexandre.

When it was time for dessert, Laure went into the kitchen to fetch it. The woman who reappeared had changed in both appearance and nationality. She had swapped the black wig for a blonde one and now called herself Katinka, a Dutch girl who spoke like a native of

Amsterdam. Her new dress revealed the curve of her hips and the swell of her bra-less breasts. She swayed provocatively, and I felt deliriously happy to possess so many fabulous creatures in one woman. This was her way of telling me I need never be bored with her, or look elsewhere.

I remember vividly the carnal abandon that followed. It looked as if Laure had won. She had resuscitated desire.

Over the days that followed Laure continued to gratify me with unexpected pleasures. She even got me into a theatre box and made me screw her in the middle of a performance. I loved all this unpremeditated love-making (well that's what it was for me anyway), but there were times when I had to moderate Laure's legitimate passion. If I had enacted all the fantasies she was driven to I would have spent every single day on her belly, sweating myself silly.

Laure could not know that her sensual persistence was in fact helping me to tame the passion I continued to feel for Fanfan. Her diligent inventiveness meant that I could now bear the frustration which, only a week earlier, I had found intolerable. Unwittingly, she was working to preserve my passion for her rival.

It is the fate of some people to be pawns in a game of chess played by others. What I had yet to discover was that this fate could be mine too. Fanfan's next offensive took me by surprise.

Fanfan phoned to invite me to dinner that Saturday at the Drugstore, Saint-Germain-des-Près. There would be no need to lie. Laure was off to see her parents and try to instil a little forgiveness into her mother. The woman's intransigence maddened her.

With a song in my heart I sped off to the drugstore – which, incidentally, was near my father's place. Fanfan had something to get off her chest and lost no time in getting down to it.

She began by telling me how difficult she found it to talk frankly about our relationship, how she was afraid I would fall back on my usual falseness and claim to feel nothing more than friendship for her. Then she explained that when, several months ago now, she had described her 'dream at Ker Emma', she never meant my courtship to last half a year – a week or two would have been plenty.

'All I was saying was that I was sick of these "Hello, nice-to-pet-you" types.'

Well, I had been warned, and since it was now impossible to deny my feelings, I simply listened in silence, astonished at this new and unexpected attempt to get everything into the open.

With great restraint, Fanfan confessed that she was violently attracted to me, but hastened to add that she had no intention of separating me from the girl Laure who had burst into my flat that day. The way she insisted on this was almost comical. Then she said how hard she found it to understand my behaviour, and described what her life had become since I began tormenting her. The euphoria she had felt at the beginning had now become a hell. Our chaste intercourse with its permanent exasperation of the senses had bled her dry. She hadn't the strength to go on with this perverse flirting – especially since, having found out about Laure, she knew it would lead absolutely nowhere.

For this reason she was asking me to stop pursuing her, to abandon my equivocation and stop hatching all these scenarios of seduction. She reiterated: our chaste intercourse with its over-excitement of the senses was wearing her out. Fanfan no longer had the strength for all this amatory banter. Now that she had found out about Laure she knew that nothing would come of it.

'And the last thing I want is to play the role of mistress,' she concluded, looking me right in the eye.

What could I do? I was distraught, but chose to ignore her warning; apologetically yet insistently, I protested that I had acted in good faith throughout and had never had any designs on her. I had always seen her as my sister, I said with consummate gall, the one I always dreamed of having. Then, with a great show of sincerity, I bemoaned the female incapacity for disinterested friendship with men.

This manoeuvre took Fanfan by surprise, and she was thrown by my apparent honesty. However, she still had enough wits about her to react with feigned enthusiasm.

'Well that's marvellous, then. All I want is for us to be friends — so long as "brother" doesn't start acting weird, okay?'

She continued, echoing the arguments I had used one night in praise of our friendship — that the purely platonic nature of our bond put it beyond the ravages of time. Roguishly, she added that we could never leave each other because we would never be 'together'.

'And we can sleep with whoever we want without betraying each other!' she said with false gaiety.

I forced a smile to hide my growing alarm. I had never wanted us to become comrades, and I had no idea how I could keep our relationship on its ambiguous footing if Fanfan refused to cooperate. Friendship, I now saw, was the enemy of our passion. I had not allowed for the idea of Fanfan's heart and body being shared and enjoyed by another man.

Even so, I was surprised by the violence of my re-action. It suddenly occurred to me that Fanfan was asking for friendship in the hope that I would refuse it. There was certainly no better way of making me take the first step as a lover. But whether her request was sincere or calculated, I had to re-establish a little fantasy and seduction between us. Fanfan might not want to, but I hadn't suffered so much just to become her 'best friend'.

In fact, the idea for my next move came from Fanfan herself, in the form of a casual remark:

'It's so hot! It'd be so nice to wake up tomorrow and find myself in Ker Emma ready for a dip in the sea.'

Upon which I told her I·had to answer a call of nature and scuttled down to the pharmacy in the drugstore basement. They knew me there. That was where I bought the sleeping pills which my father over-consumed to obtain his nightly chemical slumber. The pharmacist gave me a box of Maxi-Prohypnol, a real sledgehammer of a sedative. Then I went back to Fanfan. Seeing that she had gone to the Ladies, I took the opportunity to dissolve three sachets into her mint cordial.

When she came back she emptied her glass and told me about a project she was going to show Gabilan that was so original she just knew he would love it. Fanfan wanted to film a real love affair using a hidden camera. Only one of the two actors would know what was going on. He would follow the directions given in the script, but this would constantly be modified to allow for his partner's reactions.

'You see,' she yawned, 'I want to show passion as it really is.'

Fanfan fell asleep in the car as I was driving her home. As soon as she was unconscious I set off for Ker Emma. Life with me would be like a festival, her every dream within reach. If I could make her inhabit a fairy tale then perhaps she would think of me as her Prince Charming.

At the wheel of my father's powerful car I felt on top of the world. At last I was being myself, the unpredictable and extravagant Alexandre, the immoderate self whom I so often – too often – silenced. I could feel the blood of the Crusoés coursing through my veins and wondered at the fact that this rowdy character could coexist with an Alexandre as pusillanimous as he was level-headed. And yet both were me, the one who shared his life with Laure and the one now driving into the black night at 180 kilometres an hour to satisfy one of Fanfan's whims.

We arrived at Ker Emma at two in the morning, local time. I took the high street, past Sauvage the butcher, past Sauvage the bookseller and past the statue of Népomucène Sauvage, then parked in front of the Hôtel du Globe. Below us, the waves of the ocean pounded the sea wall.

I climbed into the hotel through the skylight and, taking Fanfan in my arms, tiptoed up to a room on the first floor. Then I undressed her. Her beauty stunned me

into surprised admiration. For a moment I felt impelled
to take advantage of the situation, to caress her and kiss
her on the lips, but I feared that the pleasure of this
contact with her body would be so intense that I would
just have to go further. So I abstained, and simply slid
her between the sheets of the bed. Then I went off to
sleep in another room.

I had no idea how Fanfan would react the next
morning. While her idea for a film revealed a real taste
for trickery, she could still have been sincere when she
said she wanted our relationship to become one of true
friendship.

I went to sleep a worried man.

I got up early and went down to the kitchen.

Monsieur Ti looked up at me in astonishment, then
nodded a greeting and offered me a bowl of coffee.
Since his gut-twisting black brew was a danger to both
stomach and heart, I declined and poured myself a cup
of tea.

'I arrived last night with Fanfan.'

This information made Ti extremely perplexed. He
remained silent for a while then, with a smile, he said,
'Now do you understand why I never mentioned her to
you?'

'Don't worry. We haven't slept together and we
never will. I don't want to. I'm getting married to Laure
in September.'

'I was right to hide Fanfan from you for as long as I
could.'

I gulped down some tea. The old buzzard drained his
bowl of coffee then, gleefully, he added, 'You can't

imagine the surprises love holds in store for you!'

And all of a sudden this usually impenetrable and reticent creature was in the middle of an astounding revelation. The night before, when they were in bed, Maude had suddenly slipped her hand into his pyjama trousers. She knew of course that his member was a weary old veteran and yet, in a moment of madness, Ti murmured, 'If it moves, take it.'

And move his prick did. Both took their fill of pleasure. Ti's pains were a searing reminder of the fact.

'Do you realize? At eighty-five years old, and for free!'

I was stunned. We were always so awkward when it came to talking about ourselves: this confidence brought us closer.

But now he was back to his normal self, the ironic Monsieur Ti. With great verve he began to relate his latest extravagance.

A fortnight earlier he had published an obituary telling of his imminent demise in the local newspaper, the *Paris-Normandie*. He announced his death for the coming week and invited the local population to a funeral to be held on that very day, a Monday.

As soon as the paper was out the news spread through Ker Emma. Monsieur Ti set about organizing his funeral with all the sprightliness of an heir. He walked around the town with a mischievous grin spread all over his face, ordering magnificent wreaths from the florist and, from the undertaker, a made-to-measure coffin for which he had several fitting sessions and insisted on having a satin lining and a lace catafalque. There was no end to his coquettish flirtation with death, and his eccentricity was a great source of amusement to his fellow inhabitants of Ker Emma. Next, Ti started visiting his friends to take messages for their dear departed. 'I'll be with them soon, so don't miss out!' The bonhomie with which he evoked his coming demise was contagious. For a whole week the people of Ker Emma spoke of death as of a friend who came bearing gifts for all. Only the curate was worried. He even betook his sorry-looking features along to Ti's place and demanded that the old man put an end to the farce. Ti said he was afraid he could not guarantee that his heart would stop beating on Monday, but assured him of his presentiment that Monday would be the big day.

This story will seem incredible to anyone who has never met Monsieur Ti, but it is true. Ti's method of overcoming his fears had always been to turn them into a joke, and his angst grew more intense as his end drew nearer. He wanted his fellow citizens to feel the shadow of death upon them as he did, and it angered him to see his contemporaries behave as if this minor hitch in the human condition didn't even exist. He wanted to give people a joyous reminder that their days were numbered. Surprise and disorientation were the twin pillars of his pedagogy.

On Sunday, the whole village was seized with the superstitious fear that Ti's prophecy would come true. And Ti, quite out of character, decided to attend Mass, where he collected emotional and valedictory hand-shakes from all present.

The next day, the obituary column of the *Paris-Normandie* announced to the people of Ker Emma that Monsieur Ti had decided to postpone his death and, to celebrate the non-interruption of his existence, was inviting his near and dear ones to drinks in the gardens of the Hôtel du Globe, at six p.m. Ti wanted to celebrate the miracle of life in the company of his friends. This gesture of defiance towards the Grim Reaper was his way of preparing for death.

Moved by Monsieur Ti's whimsical gravity, I laid out Fanfan's breakfast on a tray and went up to wake her, taking great care not to spill the orange juice or the tea.

I opened the shutters.

Fanfan stretched, arching her back with a lack of selfconsciousness that took my breath away. Fanfan was desirable even when waking up – there was no need to use the imagination. She stared, wide-eyed, and for a moment was transfixed with astonishment. I smiled.

'I'm surprised you didn't taste the sedatives I put in your mint cordial.'

She gave a hoot of laughter. 'That's just the kind of thing I'd expect from you.'

She seemed quite pleased that I had ignored what she told me the night before. Her reaction reinforced my belief that when she told me to leave her in peace she was really urging me to be a bit bolder.

As she drank her orange juice and nibbled a piece of bread and butter she scolded me playfully for having 'taken me by deceit'. The way she said 'take' was enough to suggest that I could have enjoyed her favours that very night.

'Was it you who undressed me?' she asked, just for the enjoyment of hearing me say 'Yes'.

Eager to oblige, I said 'Yes', and saw her blush with

pleasure. Then she suggested we go and take a dive in the sea. Once we got there she knew I would be easy game. I agreed. She hid herself away in the bathroom for a few minutes then emerged in a brief bathing costume, convinced that this would sweep away whatever reservations I still had.

'Shall we go?' she said, opening the window.

'Yes.'

And with that she jumped out into the void. Before I could think to hold her back she was down below, laughing on the lawn. 'Come on, jump. It's not far!'

That was Fanfan for you. A girl of mysterious ways, ruled by her whims. She was free, like a child ignorant of grown-up manners. I followed her out of the window, head over heels in love.

The June sun was imitating the July sun, but the beach was still free of the urban crustaceans who colonized the bay of Ker Emma during the holiday months. There was no one to cool our lascivious thoughts.

We bathed in the waves, where my passion cooled off slightly, then lay down on the sand to dry.

She looked at me with eyes full of words she didn't want to have to say: 'Would you mind rubbing some of this on?'

She lay on her back and handed me the tube of suntan lotion.

'This is all very provocative, what you're asking me to do here. If I didn't know you better, I might get the wrong idea.'

I took my courage in both hands and with two fingers began spreading the lotion on her shoulders. Then I made the heroic decision to go down as far as her navel, carefully avoiding her breasts on the way. Inevitably, I soon found myself swept away by lust, but refused to add a third finger because then they'd all want a go.

Fanfan closed her eyes the better to enjoy this physical contact. Her features expressed a mixture of pleasure and pain. My fingers slowed. I was in a paroxysm of longing as they followed the curves of her body. Holding back like this, I could enjoy every nuance of desire. These disingenuous caresses allowed me to discover the peaks that can be reached only through frustration. This languorous state set my senses in a spin and the torture grew more intense every second.

Fanfan bit her lower lip and I could hear her breathing grow quicker. The Fanfan I loved was divine, human and animal all in one. I feasted insatiably on the sight of her perfect body, doing my best to hide my hungry stare. With my two finger tips − yes, just two fingers! − I explored the wonder that was her beauty, trying to fathom the mystery of her incredible complexion, to penetrate the enigma of her radiance.

But my voice when I spoke was nonchalant.

'I think you could afford to lose a few kilos,' I suggested coolly.

'I know, I'm really obese.'

Fanfan half opened her eyes. A smile hovered over her lips and she put her hand close to mine. I pretended not to notice and withdrew it to flick my hair from my forehead. She smiled again. She must have felt my fingers trembling over her body and known exactly what that meant.

In an attempt to deny these treacherous tremblings I gave her a vigorous face pack of cream and, having coated her from toe to temple, lay belly-down in the sand, thus hiding both my face and the telltale bulge below my waistline.

'Why are you lying on your stomach?' she asked with childlike candour.

'To get my back brown.'

'Ah,' she said, taking off her bikini top.

Her two white breasts bounced freely before my eyes. Their colour was immodest, shocking. My pulse broke into a sprint. I was at fever pitch. Had they been as brown as her arms, my emotion would have been less intense, but the unmistakable message of their pallor was that these beauties were rarely unveiled, that it was a privilege to behold them.

My heart ached and I was dizzy with desire. I asked her to spread some cream on my back. She smiled and began oiling me, not with two fingers but with her whole hand. Ah, Fanfan's sweet little hand!

She was caressing away my resistance and when I felt her fingers falter on the back of my neck I knew it was time to put an end to the prevarication we both found so agonizing.

Fanfan put the cap on the tube and, giggling as she dabbed a blob of cream on my nose, ran towards the sea, calling out for me to follow her. Just as I was getting up I heard a voice calling my name. I turned and looked in the direction of the sea wall.

It was Laure.

This, as she told me afterwards, was another of her surprises, another attempt to astonish me and get our love back on its feet. Finding the flat empty she had phoned the Hôtel du Globe. It was Hermantrude who answered and of course she confirmed that I was at Ker Emma. A two-hour train ride later, Laure was scaling the sea wall.

And now here she was, walking towards me with a smile that vanished when she saw Fanfan emerging from the sea.

The next second was the longest I have ever lived through. Fanfan went pale. Laure was quick and clever enough not to show her jealousy. Instead she gave Fanfan a negligent glance and kissed me on the lips, then lay down beside me and, toying with my hand, told me about the wedding dress she had at last managed to track down in some couturier's shop, casually adding for Fanfan's edification that 'We're getting married four months from now.'

Fanfan was treated to Laure's lamentations over the thorny problems of preparing this happy event, her indignation at the exorbitant cost of caterers, her contempt for the bureaucratic fussiness of the town hall and her sarcasm for that of the Church.

'You really have to be in love with each other just to go through with it all,' she concluded.

'I do pity you,' said Fanfan.

Fanfan said she was very sorry but that professional obligations prevented her from staying with us a moment longer.

'Gabilan wants me in his office two days before shooting starts. I really must get back to Paris. Have a nice wedding.'

Fanfan turned on her heels and was gone. She did not kiss us goodbye.

In fact I was quite pleased that Laure had prevented

me from infringing my self-imposed law. Fear had awoken the conformist in me. If Laure had arrived a second or two later my whole life would have been shaken to its foundations. To think I had nearly given way because of a tube of suntan lotion! With this reprimand in mind, I renewed my resolution forthwith.

But Laure's arrival also satisfied the seeker and man of passion. To kiss Fanfan would be an act of madness, and if I committed it I would never again reexperience the burning ambiguity of those moments on the beach. Laure's sudden intrusion kept that burning happiness within the realm of possibility.

Poor old Laure, everything she did had the effect of sustaining my fascination for Fanfan. She would have served her cause better by encouraging us to set up home together.

Laure and I were on our way to say goodbye to Monsieur Ti when Maude stopped us.

'He said he wanted to see you alone.'

So I left Laure with Maude and set off for the office Ti had made for himself in the abandoned lighthouse that overlooks Ker Emma from the clifftop. The old buzzard had piled the place high with books. These books were his parents, they had raised him as a mother raises her child. Indeed, I believe the writers he cherished were his true parents. Up there in his lighthouse, amidst his authors, Ti felt truly at home. There he conversed with Montaigne, intervened in the ongoing quarrels between Voltaire and Rousseau, kept company with the great historians and, on occasions, recited Stendhal to Shakespeare. He saw himself as a one-man salon for authors of different centuries. Through his eyes, Musset could discover Zweig and Rabelais was able to read Swift.

I reached the clifftop and opened the lighthouse door. Ti's laughter echoed through the tower. I was surrounded by piles of slumbering novels, essays and various other texts waiting only to be awoken.

I started up the spiral staircase.

'Monsieur Ti? Are you alone?'

'No,' he replied, just as I was entering his office. 'I'm with Monsieur Rabelais.'

Ahead of me I saw books and the sea. Ti sat facing the horizon, perched on a mahogany commode he had converted into a chair.

He gestured at the shelves which lined the circular room. 'Do you see all these volumes? One day they'll all be yours. I have bequeathed them to you in my will – my library and my lighthouse – and when your time comes I would like you to do the same and leave them to the person you deem worthy of such a heritage.'

As I looked around at the thousands of books I felt deeply moved. Ti had already introduced me to most of the authors, but the sight was still awesome.

'You must be wondering if I'm not bitter at never having written any of these myself? Well, I'm not. I have used my talent in reading and collecting them. I believe that the world is even shorter of great readers than it is of great writers. To build up a library you have to be something of an architect.

'Come closer, I've something to tell you.'

I sat opposite him, on a stepladder.

Ti spoke, emphasizing each word.

'I absolutely forbid you to marry Laure.'

What right did he have to act as the sovereign arbiter of my existence? I was stung.

'Why?'

'For all the reasons you are already aware of, or are bound to discover.'

'Monsieur Ti, what I do with my life is my business. I would be grateful if you kept out of it. Thank you very much for the inheritance. Goodbye.'

I rose and headed for the door.

'Alexandre, if you do marry Laure in September you will be committing a crime against love. And that is extremely serious.'

By now I was out of the room.

Meanwhile, Laure pressed ahead with our nuptial arrangements as though this in itself would precipitate the big day. Her sights were set on 15 September, the date beyond which my interests would somehow become exclusively marital.

But though she seemed in high spirits when she ordered her taffeta dress, her behaviour betrayed a constant underlying anxiety. She was struggling to convince herself that this frothy concoction would ensure my eternal commitment, that reserving a band and hiring a caterer would forge adamantine links between our destinies.

There was something desperate about the way she wrote names and addresses on the envelopes for the invitations; but with every stamp she stuck on her worries grew lighter.

As I watched her I had the feeling it was somebody else's wedding she was organising. The only acknowledgement of my involvement in the whole thing was when she asked me to post the invitations.

On my way to the post office, I realized with a shudder that sending off these two hundred cards would carry me beyond the point of no return, or very nearly. Suddenly I was struck by the absurdity of my behaviour. I was about to marry a woman whom I had not chosen with my heart, but out of a cowardly desire to soothe my adolescent anxieties, and to keep away from the woman I feared but also loved.

I was overcome with panic. My instincts took over and I threw the invitations down a drain. It felt so good. I had made peace with myself. I had slipped back into my own skin, leaving behind the conformist persona thrust upon me by my desire for stability.

With a lighter heart I sat down at a café terrace and ordered three scoops of ice cream to celebrate the return of my sincerity. It was a moment to savour: for the first time, I was leaving behind the deceptions of a mendacious life. Ah! the joy of being honest at last.

I vowed that from now on I would always listen to what old Ti told me. Then I went home and declared, 'Laure, I've thrown the invitations into the gutter!'

At first she thought – or hoped – it was just a bad joke. Then her despondency showed in her face. Summoning up the courage to be truthful, I told her that I still wanted to live with her, but without getting married. Naturally, those who do not suffer from an irrepressible need to be loved, who are invulnerable to the pain of being disliked, will find the word courage out of place here. But if there is one thing I could not – and still cannot – bear, it is the risk of being unpleasant. The mere thought of upsetting someone makes me ill, and a critical look is tantamount to torture. I think that it hurt me as much as it did Laure to disappoint her like this, but there was no way I could go on cheating.

It was all too much for Laure to bear. She felt humiliated by my sudden change of heart, all the more so since it would soon be public knowledge. That was not what she said, of course, but her every word and expression bespoke wounded pride and disillusionment.

A few tears later her shelves were clear. Laure, and our attempt to live together, were no more than a memory in my half-empty flat.

I had been counting on Laure: now there was no one to keep me out of Fanfan's arms.

NINE

WITH LAURE GONE I HAD TO FACE THE SAD FACTS: I was no better at monogamy than my parents. But Monsieur Ti was delighted.

I now found it almost impossible to believe that a man and a woman can grow old together without facing a cruel dilemma: split up or fossilize. Laure's attempts to reinvigorate our increasingly anaemic feelings had been worthy, but in vain. Now I knew that the gangrene of time was fatal to love. Our failure strengthened my belief that it is a crime to try and lock passion within a couple. And the choice was not between a life spent in tandem or two lives lived in parallel; no, the rot of habit is something that sets in with the second kiss. Sharing the same doormat only aggravates the process.

Alone in my flat, I pondered men's strange persistence through the centuries. Why go on kissing girls and women when the debacle it leads to is common knowledge? What use is experience?

In spite of these thoughts, my passion for Fanfan had reached new heights of excitement. I had to get this carefree, joyous creature into my life, and quickly. But God knows, the emotions she provoked in me left no room for thoughts of an affair – quite the contrary, in fact.

I therefore decided that Fanfan and I would live together without her knowing it.

My plan was to work my way invisibly into her world, to share her daily life on the sly, while sustaining between us that initial desire to please each other. The actual details of this life together – a life so secret she wouldn't even know about it – were still hazy; but I was determined to take this unilateral marriage all the way.

At twenty, I was capable of adventures that now strike me as pure fiction. And yet I really was that young man, whose romantic behaviour sometimes makes me feel I have lived a part of my life in a novel.

Fanfan was bent over the plans for Gabilan's new film when I informed her I had broken off with Laure. She smiled and stepped towards me. I could see she wanted to kiss me. Her joy was written all over her face.

'But I'm in no mood to start any new relationships,' I added.

She was obviously upset, and for a moment she remained speechless. I explained the many reasons I had for not risking my affections on a new commitment. Not that my abstinence from sex with other girls was much consolation to her. The skill with which she now sought to bend my austere principles, and the acuity with which she used the most general of terms to evoke our very specific feelings, almost dislodged me from my position. However, I still had sufficient strength to insist that I had lost my faith in love and to suggest that we should proceed on the footing of brother and sister.

'After all, Ti and Maude are our shared parents aren't they?'

I pursued this line by inviting her to consider me as her big brother and recalling the night of our dinner at the drugstore, when she entreated me to put an end to what she called the 'ambiguity' of our relationship.

With a semblance of sincerity that surprised even myself, I repeated that she was the loving sister I had never had, the pillar of strength I could not do without. For which reason I preferred to maintain our affection-ate camaraderie as the surest way of never losing her. These words came straight from the mind, but although they rallied neither my senses nor my heart, I neverthe-less managed to speak them with an ersatz conviction.

Had Fanfan put her lips on mine at that moment I would have succumbed, but Fanfan didn't have the heart to force me. I had just crushed her hopes.

Fanfan complied with my request, but in a manner that should have aroused my suspicions.

Fanfan had no idea that my plans now involved more than the simple pursuit of austerity in love. I was deter-mined to become a clandestine fixture in her existence.

I spent my days dreaming of Fanfan. Naturally, I failed the September exams at Sciences-Po. Angered by this casual approach to study, my father decided that cutting off my allowance would have a salutary effect.

What with my already conspicuous pile of outstanding debts, my only remaining option was to pawn the limousine he had made the mistake of registering in my name. Titanic's suggestion was suddenly very relevant.

Those who may be astonished that it never occurred to me to earn my living should remember that all my energies were monopolized by my love life, and that none of my job prospects offered an income to match my wild outgoings.

My first step towards sharing Fanfan's existence was to take up quarters in a hotel opposite her building. From my room, I could admire her in her flat through a pair of binoculars. Apart from its somewhat over-familiar porters and lift boy, the hotel had only one defect: four stars.

The reader can easily imagine my anxiety as I crossed off the days in my appointments book, which I kept blank so as to be available for Fanfan at any moment. But in the end I paid no more attention to my outlay than would a hardened cocaine user. Sometimes I even smiled when I thought of the thrifty young lad I had been with Laure. The prospect of losing the possibility of contemplating Fanfan in her room was so upsetting that the anxiety inspired by my financial chaos was much the lesser evil.

At the end of the first week, the hotel management suggested that if I wished to stay longer I should settle the debt I had incurred thus far. I duly wrote out a cheque to cover this exorbitant bill, assuming the bland detachment of a little rich kid so as not to appear suspicious.

I had put my finger in the trap. Over these last few days I had got used to living near – if not with – Fanfan. I had marvelled at her gift for happiness whereby, instead of trying to free herself of it, she accomplished her daily round with an almost religious attentiveness. I loved her for this ability to stage-manage pleasure. Leaving the hotel would have been tantamount to leaving her. I needed to see her every day. Each night I got up several times to look at her darkened window. Imagining her sleeping, nearby, I was filled with a delicious sensation of peace.

I had told my mother I was involved in a new relationship to stop her worrying about my prolonged absence. Fanfan, meanwhile, assumed I was continuing with my studies at Sciences-Po. It never occurred to her that at the very moment she thought of me I was watching her – be it through my binoculars, a hundred metres behind her in the street, or even in the same café.

I followed her wherever following was possible. If she bought a book, I went into the shop just after she left and purchased the same edition. I wanted our minds to think the same thoughts. In the restaurant – assuming I managed to find a table out of sight – I told the waiter to bring me exactly the same dishes. Eating what she had ordered was like sharing her meal.

Anyone who takes me for a nutter has never really loved. Insanity is when you fail to go mad with love.

At the hotel, my bill grew bigger and bigger.

*

One night, with a tremble in her voice that certainly couldn't be put down to the bad line, Fanfan invited me to dinner with her parents.

'After all, if we're brother and sister then I really should introduce them to you,' she added, before hanging up.

Her mother and father had left Ker Emma two years ago. They needed to get away from the beach where Fanfan's younger sister had drowned – and to pursue their careers in a hospital in Paris. Both were lung cancer specialists. A disease which, as worthy children of Ker Emma, they had sworn to stamp out.

It was a Thursday night. I took myself along to their flat on the corner of two narrow alleys, the very existence of which is evidence that Haussmann ran out of time in his attempts to raze every building in pre-modern Paris.

Her father opened the door, pulled me towards him, and gave me a kiss.

'Alexandre, let me give you a hug! Do forgive me for calling you by your first name, but I prefer it that way. And you must call me Gilbert.'

'Good evening, Alexandre!' echoed her mother. She told me I was to call her Nathalie, then gave me a warm embrace.

With a barely-suppressed smile, Fanfan relieved my arms of the flowers I had judged it polite to bring, then disappeared with the excuse that they needed a vase.

'Make yourself at home,' said her mother, twice, as she plonked me on a sofa.

They poured me a glass of champagne.

Gilbert spoke with fatherly concern about my studies

114

at Sciences-Po and confessed that he had heard a lot about me. He spoke approvingly of my frequent visits to 'the old folk at Ker Emma' – viz, Maude and Monsieur Ti. Then he thanked me for having put Fanfan in contact with Gabilan through the good offices of my father.

'You're exactly as she described you,' declared Nathalie.

I was still trying to account for all this gushing affection and earnest concern when Nathalie mentioned a ring I had apparently offered to their daughter in a gesture of 'wild extravagance'.

Gilbert obligingly spelt it out for me:

'So tell me, where exactly did you celebrate your engagement?'

I was open-mouthed with astonishment.

'Dad, I've told you before that we were alone. There was no one else,' answered Fanfan, reappearing with the vase.

'Yes, but where were you?'

'In Vienna,' she said coolly.

'Vienna?' Her mother turned to look at me.

'Uh, yes,' I confirmed. 'It's more . . . well, it was more romantic.'

Fanfan took over:

'He asked me when we were at a ball. In the middle of a waltz.'

'I didn't know they still went in for those grand balls in Vienna?'

'Oh yes, yes.' I gave Fanfan a startled look. She smiled back.

This was the bitch's way of telling me that however satisfied I might be with the current status quo she, for one, was not and would not leave it unchallenged: she was taking the initiative. I realized that I should have seen it coming when she described her project of filming a love story, with one of the partners manipulating the other in front of a hidden camera.

Having recovered from my initial astonishment, I decided to play the game. I had no objection if people considered Fanfan and myself to be a couple. After all, as far as I was concerned, it was the truth, one I tried to illustrate by sharing Fanfan's existence without her knowledge. The main thing was that I should still seem reticent about her, that she should remain in a state of passionate impatience.

Things got even more embarrassing around the dinner table, when her parents asked about the date of our wedding. I sensed that Fanfan had suggested this question beforehand.

But Fanfan made no effort to help me. She just stretched her pretty neck and rested her chin non-chalantly in her hand, watching me and waiting for my answer with undisguised interest.

'Um?'

I was crimson, tongue-tied. If Fanfan had lied to her parents, then that was her responsibility, but I had no intention of setting a date for a marriage I refused to even contemplate. If I did there would be no going back, unless of course I repeated the volte-face I had inflicted on Laure. And once had been enough.

The confidence of my reply came as a real surprise to me:

'Well, what Fanfan probably hasn't told you is that I'm currently going through divorce proceedings. I suppose you'll think twenty's a bit young to have been married and divorced, but that's how it is. I'd rather wait until the whole thing's over before thinking about our wedding.'

Fanfan gave me a discreet nod, as if to acknowledge my resourcefulness, then looked away.

Afterwards I drove her back to her flat, the flat I thought of as being ours. Sitting in the car, she tried to justify her behaviour:

'You know, my parents are a bit old-fashioned. They're always trying to find out if I've got some man on the go. Now they'll leave me in peace. And you're not committed to a thing.'

'Why didn't you warn me?'

'Because you wouldn't have come.'

'And the ring?'

'I bought it on credit. If you want to offer it to me one day you can always pay off the debt.'

I dropped Fanfan off outside her abode, taking great care to kiss her only on the cheeks, then went back to my hotel room after a detour to avoid reception. My bill was sky high, but the sum seemed so unreal it actually served to soothe my anxiety. Six thousand francs unpaid was worrying, forty-five was way beyond my frame of reference. I had reached the point where you give up worrying and wait for a miracle.

In her room, Fanfan was combing her hair. I saw her slip into bed and open the first volume of Chateaubriand's *Mémoires d'Outre-Tombe*, which she – and I – had just bought. I got into bed and took out my copy, hoping that this simultaneous reading would plunge us into shared sensations.

A few pages later, I was overwhelmed by the stupidity of my behaviour. My sweet Fanfan was lying there only a hundred metres away, ready at the slightest sign to be mine, and here I was forcing myself to sleep alone in a place where each new day dug me deeper into ruin. I sprang out of bed, threw on some trousers, a shirt and some moccasins, and ran over to Fanfan's building.

The main door was shut fast with a security lock and I didn't know the code. I grumbled to myself at the Parisian mania for fitting buildings with such devices: the only people they successfully kept out were friends and lovers come to surprise their sweethearts.

Like any competent burglar, I decided to wait until an ingoing or outgoing person gave me the chance to slip through behind them. My shirt, however, was of fine material and I soon found myself suffering in the autumn wind. It was ten minutes to midnight, and still no one came – only doubts by the dozen. I drove them away, but the cold was beginning to get to me. In the end it drove me to the conclusion that I had not cancelled my marriage with Laure only to leap straight into a new commitment. After a quick tour through my memory I was unable to come up with a single couple of fifty-year-olds who still burned with the desire to kiss each other. Most of them were divorced and the survivors were a disgrace to love. Monsieur Ti and Maude were, of course, a special case. They would die before their flame could be snuffed out.

I beat a retreat, aware that I was no better suited than my contemporaries to conjugal passion. My failure with Laure was proof enough of that. I could not bring myself to repeat the risky attempt to live as a couple. Fanfan was not a phase, but the love of my life. And that was why I had no right to take any chances.

That night, as I fell asleep, I was blissfully unaware that the very next morning the hotel management would demand full payment of my bill.

As I settled the bill presented to me at reception, I calculated that I had at least forty-eight hours before my cheque went through.

I therefore had two days to inflate my account, after which the bank would most certainly lay its hands on my father's car.

I phoned Titanic and asked him to take me to a secret gambling den. That very night he led me to a dive where they knew him by the name of Monsieur Anatole.

The place was swarming with clammy, sweating humans. Even the non-smokers were smoking. In the eyes of the men who had fetched up here there was a harsh glint of excitement, inspired by games about which I didn't know the first thing. They were swapping cards and smiles without gaiety. They came from Algiers – from poverty – and from elsewhere, and yet the tables were piled high with money.

In a mirror I caught the image of myself amidst this motley crew, and I was shocked to see myself here. Was this the same young man who, only a few months ago, was dreaming of a respectable existence? What would Laure say if she could see me here?

My pockets contained the sum total of my hopes, three thousand francs. For a moment I felt like running away. A sickly young man had just chanced his last banknote, and luck had just whisked it away. Suddenly his eyes seemed to black out. The sight made me shiver. Nevertheless, I stayed with Titanic. Backing out was a luxury I could no longer afford.

Titanic was explaining to me why roulette was his favourite form of fear but I didn't hear. Instead I let instinct be my guide and laid my three thousand francs in the middle of the baize.

'You've won,' said Titanic sadly.

When I opened my eyes my three thousand francs had become sixty thousand. I stuffed them into my pockets as fast as I could, without questioning what had happened.

'Hey,' I whispered, 'let's get out of here fast!'

My gleanings from the green table would fill the yawning chasm of debt caused by fifteen nights in the hotel.

But Titanic had no desire to leave. We'd only just arrived, he insisted. Titanic couldn't bear good luck, and happiness made him tense.

What happened next is a mystery to me. All I know is that I lost all my winnings and made my bank balance sink by a further twenty thousand francs.

Three days later they impounded my father's car. I was still residing at the hotel, whose management knew nothing of my financial plight. My cheque had been honoured. My only consolation in all this distress was my observation of Fanfan from a distance. Loving her was all I lived for. At night, I got up several times to go and gaze at her window. Although she was hidden by the darkness I felt as though I was watching over her sleep.

On Friday at six p.m. I made my worried way to my

father's place. He was expecting me to give him his car back. I rang at the door. He opened it. He had the telephone in his hand and was wearing a moth-eaten old dressing gown.

I went into his office and sat down, and waited for him to stop vociferating into the mouthpiece. The conversation revolved around the usual subjects of ruin: taxes, women and cinema. Dad promised his interlocutor imminent death if he failed to administer the enemas he had recommended to him immediately.

'So, how's tricks, Sandro?' he asked as he hung up.

'Dad, the bank has taken your car.'

'My car?'

'Yes, it was a security.'

'My car! Have you gone mad?'

'Yes, I'm in love with this woman, she's the love of my life.'

This was enough to stop him dead in his tracks, so I pressed on and told him about how I met Fanfan, how love at first sight had blown away my common sense, and about the solution I had thought up to prevent our love from lapsing into the inertia to which so many couples end up resigning themselves. Then I told him of my desire to live, unsuspected, with Fanfan, which subject led naturally to the expensive hotel that had become home to Alexandre the passionate voyeur.

'And that's all there is to say.'

He sighed. His voice became grave.

'I'm going for a piss.'

Dad was a man who liked to do his serious thinking while emptying his bladder. Which left me with five minutes to pace up and down and round and round his office, chewing over my apprehension at his likely re-action.

At last the toilet door opened. My father stepped forward and, impelled by an abrupt surge of emotion, clasped me to him.

By a series of hints and allusions, he made me realize that he had always thought of me as a conformist, a thoroughly uneccentric young man who was careful to avoid getting scorched by the fires of the Absolute. He had been saddened by my desire to marry Laure, but my new plan had shown him that I was an authentic Crusoé, just like himself.

The car was already forgotten: my father had just been reunited with one of his sons.

'Come on, I'm taking you round to see Mado. We've got something to celebrate.'

'Who's Mado?'

'A brothel keeper, the genuine article. I want you to meet her. It's important.'

He grabbed his keys and pushed me towards the door.

'Dad, I really don't feel like going to a whorehouse. I may be a Crusoé, but my way is different from yours.'

'Alexandre, we're not going there to make love! We're going so you can meet Mado.'

He took me by the sleeve and hauled me out.

The taxi drew up in front of a dignified, bourgeois-looking building in the Rue de Naples. Dad had forgotten his wallet so I paid the fare with my last fifty francs.

'This is the place,' he murmured.

'The place for what?'

'You'll see.'

'How are we going to pay? I haven't got a centime.'

'My dear boy, payment chez Mado takes the form of manuscripts and chapters. Her cash box is full of novels. It's a literary brothel!'

'A literary brothel?' This was most alarming.

'The customers are all writers. You go there when you've lost your way in your book. Mado reads it, then shouts her head off at you for a bit to make you spit out exactly what it is you're trying to say. After that you go and screw one of her girls as a pick-me-up.'

'But I don't want to be a writer,' I exclaimed in terror.

'Oh stop whingeing and come on.'

We passed through the main entrance.

'But . . . why does Mado do all this?'

'She's a literary agent as well as a brothel keeper. She passes her manuscripts on to a publisher and clips a ten per cent commission off the author's earnings. That's how her whorehouse works.'

When we reached the third floor my father rang the bell. The door opened to reveal Mado dressed in a black sack of a dress. She looked as if she weighed at least a hundred kilos. The expression in her eyes was that of an incredibly sensitive and intelligent dinosaur, and it frightened me. I knew at once that this was a woman you could never cheat.

'Pascal darling!' she exclaimed as she kissed my father.

'This is Alexandre, one of my sons.'

I panicked and ran back down the stairs, followed by my father's shouts:

'Hey, come back, you're a natural writer!'

'Oh, leave him alone,' came Mado's reply. 'At least now he knows where to find me.'

Back in the street I renewed my oath never to touch a pen and to steer clear of blank sheets of paper.

Looking out from my hotel window I had noticed that the flat next to Fanfan's had fallen empty. When I went to see the concierge she told me that the owner wanted to rent it out. His ad was due to appear in the next day's paper.

Dad was delighted to give me the deposit. He told me, and he seemed sincere, that he was deeply moved by my romance. I signed the lease and moved in that very night. My plan was to put a two-way mirror in the place of Fanfan's ordinary one, which was fixed to the wall separating our two flats. This way I could enjoy the illusion of living with Fanfan, while she would remain unaware of what I saw.

The project enchanted my father, and he came round to take a look at my place with a set designer from the cinema whom he had known for many years, Pierre Volux. Pierre's face was half hidden by beard and his body by fat. He was a fast worker and frequently made excellent suggestions.

Dad explained the situation to him. Volux listened wide-eyed and then grunted.

'You're mad,' he concluded, 'but not mad enough. For the kid to feel he's really living with the girl I should transform this flat into an exact replica of the one next door, to create a unity; and then I'll have to work out some kind of hatch in the ventilation system so he can hear what she's saying and the music she's listening to.'

124

I acquiesced, and so did Dad. Then, with a laugh, Volux added that as for payment, he could wait until the film made from this experiment was out on the screens. My father made an inadequate attempt to conceal the embarrassment written all over his face.

'What's all this about a film?' I asked.

He confessed that ever since he had heard about my romance he couldn't stop thinking about turning it into a film. Now I knew why he had been so eager to guarantee my rent. I protested vigorously. He had no right to steal my life.

'And what gave you the right to put my car up as security like that?' he retorted. 'It cost me one hundred and fifty thousand francs. And how do you expect me to pay for this work on the room? For Christ's sake, get down off your cloud will you!'

In exchange for this slice of my youth, Dad was offering to forget about the car, to pay for the building work and to cover my rent for a year, during which time he would provide me with a monthly allowance of two thousand francs, to enable me to cultivate my passion undisturbed. He thus estimated that the story would need twelve months to develop. As for me, I now understood as never before the true nature of writers: they are neither fathers nor husbands, nor are they wives, brothers, sisters, sons or daughters; all they are, I am afraid, is WRITERS.

I had my back to the wall. I therefore agreed to let him have these months of my biography, but on one condition: I would not allow the film to be shot until I had clarified my position regarding Fanfan, and I forbade my father to either reveal or suggest to me the appropriate ending to what, after all, remained my own story. I wasn't having someone else scripting the denouement.

The writer accepted my terms. We shook on it. I could feel myself becoming a character in a fiction.

Now we had to wait for Fanfan to be away for a good while so that we could break through a part of the common wall, put in the two-way mirror and redecorate my studio. Every time I returned home I shrank into the shadows of the stairwell, in case Fanfan saw me.

A little while later she had to go away for eight days of location hunting in Italy. I offered to water her plants over the weekend and she gave me her keys. Volux's boys did their work quickly, in forty-eight hours — set builders in the cinema are used to working to deadlines that expire before they are set.

The result was exactly as Volux had described it. He had even inverted the layout of my flat in relation to Fanfan's, as if we really were living on different sides of a mirror. Fanfan's things had been put back exactly where we found them. Volux had taken photographs of every detail before beginning to tamper with the room.

Seen from my flat, it was as if our two rooms were one and the same flat. I just had to wait for the return of my new flatmate.

Fanfan came back on Thursday evening.

She walked into her flat, glanced at her answering machine and began listening to the messages. I could breathe, she hadn't noticed anything unusual. Then she took off her skirt. Dressed only in tights and a blouse, she prepared her dinner and got out a tray. On my side,

I likewise set out my cutlery on a tray. I wasn't hungry but I enjoyed acting as if I were her reflection in a mirror. It made me feel I was her missing half.

Fanfan now finished undressing and slipped on a big loose shirt. I was roused by the fleeting glimpse of her nudity. I don't doubt that there are women with more beautiful bodies, but hers had the unique attraction of forbidden fruit that could one day come within reach.

When her meal was ready she took the tray to bed, slipped under the sheets and turned on the television. I took my empty tray and lay on my bed, two metres away from hers. I wasn't hungry for food, but for her.

Almost side by side, we watched a film from the forties. I had opened the air vent so I could hear the sound and kept my eyes glued on her screen. I was discovering the tremendous pleasure there is to be had sharing a woman's existence. I really thought I had found the magic formula.

This way, I was satisfying my need to live with her and yet doing nothing to fray the ties between us. Our idyllic romance would be devoid of domestic worries. There would be no need to tolerate our differences. We could relax fully without feeling the slightest discomfort at the presence of the other. I was freed from the guilt I used to feel when, at the end of the day, I would meet up with a lover and be too tired or preoccupied to want to listen to her. At such times I felt I was unworthy of her love. But this evening everything had taken on a new meaning. Watching television did not mean that we had nothing to say to each other. On the contrary, the impossibility of talking made me want to engage her in an all-night discussion. Untouchable, Fanfan became even more desirable – if that was possible. I was thrilled by this daily life which was anything but everyday. I had the sensation that our passion could go on like this until we died.

Yes, it was a bizarre situation, but also an exhilarating one for this heir of the Crusoés. At last, I was living life in harmony with my folly. At last, I was changing the reality I so loathed.

Gradually, I found myself forgetting the glass panel that separated us. When a commercial break broke into the film I shut the hatch and addressed myself to Fanfan:

'You see, I want our romance to be as perfect as this film. I want us to be witty at least ten times a day, and never to have to piss or shit, I want you always to be dressed like a queen, sublimely made up from morning to night, constantly well lit, and I want even our rows to be stylish. I adore you too much to put our love into practice. You are right to love the cinema: editing can redeem anything. Boring spells can be snipped away with scissors, snick, snick, snick! Only the best bits are kept. And then there's the music. But in real life, well ... I bet you that at the end of the film Bogart'll kiss Katharine Hepburn. Well, that's a mistake they won't catch us making. We may not be characters in a film but we are going to have the best, and only the best. I swear we are. Kisses have to be dreamed about, waited for ... You know I'm right, don't you? Just look around. Couples spend all their time harking back to that time of anticipation, the time of waiting for a sign of the other's love. Well, I'm not going to let that magic slip away.'

At the end of the film, Fanfan switched off the light and the television. We were separated by darkness. To revive the miracle of her presence I called her over the phone. She turned on her beside lamp and picked up the handset. My angel was visible again.

'Hello, it's me, Alexandre. I'm not disturbing you am I?'

'No, no . . .'

'You weren't trying to get to sleep?'

'No, I was reading.'

I proposed that she accompany me to Ker Emma that weekend. She accepted. I was dying to extend our almost conjugal existence with long and intimate discussions. I wanted her to provoke me, to take my anxieties by storm. I was crazy about the intellectual audacity of this daughter of the sea wall. With her I felt somehow obliged to be clever and droll. Thanks to the training of her adoptive grandfather, she could not tolerate woolly thinking. The mere fact of holding her attention made me feel intelligent.

After I had hung up, I was suddenly overcome with doubt. What did it mean, this life we led on our respective sides of the mirror? Wasn't I in the process of losing touch with the material world? But I soon obviated this troublesome thought and got ready for sleep.

Up until then, I had never imagined that Fanfan might escape me. Frustrating her seemed to me the surest way of keeping her. Oh God what a fool I was!

TEN

I MET FANFAN AT SAINT LAZARE STATION, AT THE
end of the platform. Between us and Ker Emma there
lay three hours of ambiguous intimacy. I had come
specially prepared for the journey with a repertoire of
carefully balanced utterances designed to excite her
emotions without confirming her hopes. But I had to
cast them aside when Fanfan announced: 'I've got a
surprise for you. I told Jacques to come.'

'Who is he?'

'Well it seemed the natural thing for my big brother
to make the acquaintance of my friend. Don't you
agree?'

'Your friend?'

'Yes ... my friend. He's an actor. He's working on
one of Gabilan's films. I'm sure you'll like him.'

A head bobbed above the river of passengers. The

man gestured towards us and called out Fanfan's name. She turned round. They kissed, at more than sufficient length to sting me into jealousy.

'Hello,' said Jacques in a warm voice.

'Jacques, this is Alexandre, my older brother.'

I growled a 'Hello' in response to Fanfan's introduction and forced myself to smile.

This great hulk was crushingly beautiful, almost intimidatingly so, but he seemed unaware of his radiance. His simplicity and gentleness went straight to my heart. I hated him at once, with all my soul.

On the train, the more charming he became the more I felt galled. How could I fight this thirty-year-old breath of fresh air? I had no choice but to like him. He spoke in his own special idiosyncratic language. For him, kids were 'bunnies', an elegant outfit was 'dazzling apparel', and a cat a 'scratch and sniff'. He spoke of his childhood as a war orphan and of the birds that he had secretly cared for in the dormitories of the Assistance Publique charity homes. You could see that Fanfan was moved and happy as she listened to him.

She had called him 'my friend', thus leaving their relationship shrouded in mystery. If I had been certain that this man was her lover I would have suffered, but at least I could have fought back and tried to outmanoeuvre him. As it was, I was riddled with doubt.

Maude came to pick us up at the station in her jeep. She had a real passion for this vehicle which enabled her to venture off the beaten track.

We lunched without Monsieur Ti. He had locked himself away at dawn in his lighthouse with some packets of biscuits and did not want to be disturbed.

Maude took advantage of his absence to relate a recent adventure. She knew that old Ti would not have liked to hear about it. It would have made him feel inadequate, unable to fuel her dreams.

Maude had gone off on her own to buy some dresses in Caen. She was walking in the street when she saw a very pretty blonde who looked about eighteen. A little while later, she noticed an attractive young man following the girl. She was intrigued, and decided to follow the young man to find out how it would all end. She wanted to know if love would emerge victorious. And so, despite her eighty-seven years, she trotted along like this for almost an hour, until the rather wet, feckless youth asked a policeman to get the 'old woman' who was 'on his tail' off it.

'What was he afraid of? I mean, I wasn't going to rape him, was I?' concluded Maude with a laugh.

After the meal we set off in the jeep to fetch Monsieur Ti from his lighthouse. Ti greeted us with one of his papal salutes, clambered into the vehicle and strapped on his helmet. We sped seawards, onto the beach, from which the low tide seemed to have banished the Atlantic to beyond the horizon for good.

Maude was well acquainted with the sea floor of Ker Emma bay, its shifting sandbanks and subaqueous valleys that the incoming ocean covered at the speed of a galloping horse. It was like driving under the sea, surrounded by rocks and giant seaweed.

It was a ride that Ti and Maude often took, going out to fish for crabs and prawns. Half an hour later we stopped beside a wreck buried beneath seaweed and shellfish. This skeleton of a boat lay in front of the entrance to a dark cave, a place invaded by the waves at high tide. Ti and Maude went inside carrying torches. Maude claimed this was where the biggest crabs were to be found.

Fanfan, Jacques and myself started exploring the wet dunes, hunting for prawns. Before and behind us, we could see neither earth nor sea. This maritime Sahara was strewn with kelp and dotted with jagged rocks. We had to be back at the car by six, forty-five minutes before the tide was due to come in again.

I had half-filled my bucket with crustaceans when I realized that Jacques and Fanfan had disappeared. Goaded by jealousy, I started out in search of them. I was walking further and further away from the jeep, without noticing that my footprints were soon swallowed by the wet sand.

'Fanfan!' I cried out – but my voice was lost in the wind.

Arriving at a lake of sea water it suddenly struck me that I was lost. I felt a twinge of nervousness. A few metres away, a giant octopus was ambling along slowly. I stepped back in fright. I was a prisoner of this salty wilderness, and of my own anxiety. Which way should I turn? I had no idea. And I was overcome with fear at the thought of dying before I could give Fanfan a child.

I made a panic-stricken decision to step out in what I thought was the right direction. At moments I thought I recognized certain points, but in fact I was even further off course. These underwater landscapes were all the same. At six o'clock, I visualized the scene of my drowning, devoured by crabs picking at my flesh with their pincers, or by that sinister octopus which had given me such a fright. God, how stupid I had been to keep putting off my declarations of love, and how bitterly I regretted not having known at least one night of wild abandon with Fanfan. I swore there and then that if Providence rescued me from this trap I would kiss her that very same night. But my oath seemed derisory: like my calls for help, it was carried away in the wind.

At six-thirty, I was convinced: I'd had it. The others would surely be back on the coast by now. Overcome with horror at my impending doom, I sat limply on a rock and prepared for death. Overhead, the seagulls wheeled about like vultures. There was no way I would be able to keep swimming for long in the currents of cold water that were about to submerge me. It was the beginning of May. My only consolation was to think that I would always be the Desired One of Fanfan's imagination. Indeed, it could be said that I had achieved my aim of perpetuating the passion between us until death did us part. Hades would save us from temptation.

But suddenly my whole being stirred in revolt against the idea of dying just when mortal danger had opened my eyes. I had finally understood that it is vital to live out one's aspirations. If I died, what use would this lesson have been to me?

My musings were interrupted by a low growling sound that made me freeze with fear. The ocean was coming. But then I heard the motor of the jeep. Fanfan was still searching for me.

'I'm here!' I shouted, jumping to my feet.

I was in a small valley. At the other side, I could see the swell of the waters. The murky flood rolled towards me along the sand, gathering strength as it came closer.

I turned tail and ran, reaching the top of a hill. The wave arrived at the first rocks, smashed against them, then swept on towards a natural dyke, retreating in a fury of foam. A huge expanse of froth was all that was left of this giant wave. The noise of the motor grew distant. All around me, the incoming tide continued to invade the plain of sand. My limbs stiffened with fear. I was twenty, I didn't want to leave this life so early.

Further away, the waves were massing for a new, more powerful attack. I scrambled into another depression only to find myself facing a fearful, churning breaker, bearing down on me at speed. I turned, was forced to swim several metres in the numbing water, and at last reached the sand where the trace of two jeep treads was rapidly vanishing. Fanfan had been there only moments before!

Behind me, the tide was swollen by a storm just discernible out to sea. I ran headlong in the direction of the coast – and, for all I knew, towards a water-filled hollow. The shore was still too distant to be visible. Behind me, the rollers gave chase, their foam licking at my feet as they petered out. I ran straight ahead, dreading that each step would land me in quicksand.

It was old Ti who spotted me. Fanfan was driving. She had insisted on continuing the search even when reason and safety dictated that they give up. I collapsed in the jeep, choking from my exertions, and the tears flooded down my cheeks.

As the salty waters flowed, I thought of my vow, to kiss Fanfan that very night if Providence rescued me from my predicament.

*

Back at the hotel, Maude made sure I went to bed early. Then she prepared the adjacent room for Fanfan and Jacques, as if her granddaughter had told her that Jacques was indeed her official lover. Now everything was clear.

It was torture to see the two of them disappear together for the night. The time for declarations had come and gone, and I was left to curse myself for having let Fanfan slip through my fingers. She must have had enough of my prevarication and of her own futile suffering.

All night long I had to endure the sound of Fanfan's groaning and moaning. The wall between us was paper-thin, and Fanfan was one of those girls who like their coitus loud. The rising tide had struck terror into my soul, but that was nothing to the sheer distress I felt to hear her fornicating with Jacques. I almost began to regret that destiny had saved me from the waters only to inflict such an ordeal on me. I cried with rage.

The next day, Fanfan was utterly charming towards me, and so was Jacques. I detested their niceness and their expressions of complicity. We went out for a walk along the cliffs: they spent the whole walk holding hands or with their arms around each other's waists, quite oblivious to my presence. Jacques brought up the general subject of children. Fanfan seemed moved and said that she wanted four. I reacted by scoffing at women whose only aim in life is to breed, the broody battery hens who lock themselves into maternity. Of course, my every word was prompted by spite. Had it fallen to me to be the father of these kids, you can be sure I wouldn't have been satisfied with fewer than ten.

At the foot of Monsieur Ti's lighthouse, on the clifftop, Fanfan affected a detached manner and addressed these words to Jacques: 'Tell him . . .'

'No, tell him yourself.'

'Well, it's like this. Jacques and I are going to get married in six months' time, and we'd like you to be our best man. Would you like that?'

Before us, empty space, a hundred metres below, rocks: for one moment I felt like pushing them off. Indeed, I did take a few steps forward, but then I retreated again. I had had a thought. If Jacques became her husband, then there would be a vacancy for a lover, a lover protected by that same husband from the banality of daily life which I so loathed. Their marriage would give me licence to possess Fanfan.

'Yes.' I replied with a smile.

But, not long afterwards, on our way back to the hotel, these same thoughts filled me with utter disgust. My calculating attitude reeked of Verdelot's emotional swamp. At the same time, as if by revelation, I saw the unwritten rules of my parents' amatory games. My parents had maintained their steady stream of extra-curricular affairs in an attempt to remain lover and mistress to each other. My mother adored my father and could not accept him as a mere husband, and he was too passionate about her to consider her as a wife. My mother's lovers were her real husbands. As for my father he had never been a husband, not even with his mistresses.

These inversions had caused me intense anguish in my adolescence, and I fiercely rejected them. But what role was I to play in Fanfan's life now?

Saturday night brought another ordeal as I lay listening to her incredibly clamorous orgasms. Hunched in bed, I gritted my teeth while Fanfan panted and panted and panted. Jacques was no mean shafter.

During these terrible hours I experienced the kind of distress which makes suicide seem a definite possibility. By midnight I could take no more: I hammered on the wall with my fist. The noise stopped. I took comfort in the thought that my knocking had embarrassed Jacques and upset him in full flight.

The day after that we returned to Paris. I dined alone in a café below 'our place' and despaired at my decision to have fitted that two-way mirror, for now it would force me to witness the spectacle of their nightly copulation. I didn't dare go back up to sleep for fear of finding them hot on the job. I had seen Jacques going into the building. At midnight, the owner of the bistro requested that I take myself off. They were closing.

Slowly, I mounted the stairs to our flats, opened my door and lay down on the bed, forbidding myself to look at the mirror. To avoid doing so I buried my face in the pillow.

But then a strange dialogue made me prick up my ears. Their words were wafting through the ventilation hatch, which I had forgotten to close. Jacques sounded as if he were drunk.

'No!' I heard Fanfan shout. 'Now get out of here!'

'Shit!' he yelled, 'You make me spend two whole nights pretending to make love to you, you excite me with your groaning, and then when I get interested you shut up shop.'

'Jacques, you've been overdoing the drink again. Leave

me now. I asked you a favour, that's all.'

Jacques gave an idiotic laugh:

'So, the wedding's off, huh?'

'Look, you played your part to perfection, and I'm grateful. I've got what I wanted. Alexandre is mad with jealousy, he's about to explode. So now we can stop the make-believe. Okay?'

Happiness flooded through me. I looked up and watched the scene beyond the looking glass. Jacques's face was split by a hideous grimace and his eyes seemed to swim in their sockets. Pouring scorn on the gentle, thoughtful character that Fanfan had made him play over the weekend, he bellowed that for two days he had been prevented from screwing and boozing, and that now he had had enough. I was shocked by his vulgarity. Fanfan's imaginary man, with his love of birds and fine shirts, was a million miles away from this spineless, pisshead actor with his loutish clothes. That perfect rival had been a mirage. Fanfan had managed to bring out the charm that lay dormant within the brute. What an extraordinarily talented director she was, my dear Fanfan, to have fomented so convincing a stratagem with so unbecoming an individual. If I hadn't been one step ahead in trickery, I would have gone on being taken in.

Fanfan opened the door of her flat.

'Go on, get out!' she said firmly.

Jacques kicked it shut again.

'Bitch! You got me excited, and now I'm going to have my way.'

Upon which he caught hold of Fanfan and tried to push her onto the bed. She kneed him in the crotch. He was furious, he slapped her. She bit him. Seconds later they were rolling around on the floor.

I was in a quandary. How should I react? I could certainly intervene – I had kept Fanfan's key – but how would I explain such a sudden and miraculous apparition? Now Jacques was yanking up Fanfan's skirt. I took the key from a drawer in my desk. Fanfan struggled free. He pushed her up against the mirror. I saw her face flattened against the glass. She seemed to be looking straight at me.

Throwing caution to the winds, I dashed out onto the landing, opened Fanfan's door and threw myself onto this hulk of a Jacques as he tried to force himself between Fanfan's locked legs.

'What's he doing here?' he mumbled as he got up.

My answer to this question was a headbutt. I had broken his nose and the blood flowed freely. I grabbed him by the shoulders and threw him onto the stairs, slamming the door behind him. Fanfan staggered to her feet and, without a word, threw herself into my arms. It was impossible to say which of us was trembling the most.

'My little sister,' I murmured, 'it looks as if your marriage may be off.'

'But what are you doing here?'

My answer took even me by surprise: 'I dreamt that a man was trying to rape you. I woke up with the feeling that my nightmare was actually happening, so I ran all the way here.'

Fanfan then suggested that such presentiments occur only when two people are bound by true love.

'A brother's love for his sister,' I said with a smile.

She claimed she needed to be reassured and asked me to stay next to her pretty body until morning. But I left as soon as I could.

'I have to be up with the birds tomorrow.'

In truth, I distrusted myself too much to stay with her. She looked at me as if I were a genuine Prince Charming who had dropped down from the skies to save her. Such comfort was more than welcome after the tear-stained weekend she had inflicted on me.

Back in my own flat, I watched her through the two-way mirror. Yes, this was the woman who made me feel alive all right. The performance she had obtained from Jacques that weekend was a perfect illustration of her ability to reveal people's hidden, slumbering qualities. Wherever she looked, Fanfan brought out the best in people.

As I was reflecting on all this I had an idea for getting even closer to her – as ever, without her knowing it. I planned to put it into practice the very next day.

By six-thirty in the evening I had already taken up position underneath Fanfan's bed. Gradually, in spite of the suffocating dust, I learnt to put up with my discomfort and claustrophobia. There were twenty centimetres between the underside of the bedstead and the carpet. Much to my misfortune, the rooms in this building were heated through the floor, and so I braised away in my sweat and made myself heartily nauseous by chewing on fluff. Yet I was almost happy to be suffering for love. I felt like a hero performing great exploits for the sake of his belle.

My aim and desire was to sleep with Fanfan without

touching her, to remain under her all night long. I wanted to breathe in the perfume of her body, to hear her sighs and bask in her presence – to steal in upon her intimacy. I was sure this was possible because I remembered how, when we were still together, Laure surprised one of her friends by hiding under her bed.

Beads of sweat gathered on my face, my lungs laboured to get their fill, but I knew that this position would provide me with more excitement that night than any husband in Europe could hope for with his wife. Four hours of waiting it took me, two hundred and forty minutes, in the course of which my desire for Fanfan grew to an almost hallucinogenic intensity.

The only real worry was my ceaselessly swelling bladder. I kept myself from drinking so as not to fill it any further. I forbade myself to use the toilet: if Fanfan came in and found me there my suffocating vigil would have been in vain. When the pain became unbearable, I relieved myself into a plastic bag. I twice gave myself permission to take a swig of water so as not to faint. The bottle of mineral water I had brought with me was a constant temptation.

At about ten o'clock, I began to fret, thinking she might not be coming home for the night. But I remained hidden and immobile. My hellish wait was enough to justify a little more perseverance.

At ten-thirty, the door opened. Two voices rang out in the hall and for a moment I thought Fanfan had company. But it was her other neighbour. They were saying goodnight. Then Fanfan closed her door. I sighed, as silently as I could.

Fanfan slipped off her shoes and her socks. All I could

see were her small, naked feet and her tapering ankles. This was enough for me to picture the pleasing grace of her legs. She unbuttoned her jeans and slid them down her thighs. When they slumped onto the floor I could see that they also contained her panties, which she had removed with the same gesture. Now the sight of her naked calves was even more exciting. I found it almost impossible to go on holding my breath. My loins were on fire.

Fanfan removed her blouse and bra and dropped them negligently on the carpet, then cleaned her teeth and got into bed. She left her lamp on and flicked through a magazine. Above my head, through the springs of the mattress, I trained my eyes on the gently bulging imprint made by her body as it rested on the mattress. Slowly, I raised my hand, threading it between the coils to caress her form with the tips of my fingers. I was trembling with lust. My penis was wedged tightly in my trousers: had I been able to extricate it, it would certainly have pierced a hole in the canvas of the mattress.

As the night drew to an end, I fell asleep, weary with lust and aware that the moments of bliss I had just experienced were worlds away from the common and often meagre pleasure I had known in the arms of other girls.

The next day I got back under Fanfan's bed at five o'clock. She arrived at around eight, undressed and went straight to bed. I revelled in this regained close- ness, eagerly surveying each feature of the titillating underwear she had strewn carelessly on the floor. There was only one little problem: she had donned a night dress.

143

A few minutes later, Fanfan began to speak aloud. She had not touched the phone. I was astonished, and listened with all the more attention:

'Last night I could feel something strange in the flat, like a presence, but I didn't take any notice of it. At about four in the morning though, I was woken up by the sound of snoring. I assume therefore that I was not alone.'

She paused. I had been found out, and I was deeply disappointed. My plans had been brought to nothing. Fanfan was now conscious of the full extent of my passion. No longer could I maintain between us that delicious ambiguity which made every look a moment to cherish.

'You know it would be marvellous,' she continued, 'if you came and lay down beside me, at last.'

I decided to go for broke.

I got out from under the bed, gave her a long look and, still without speaking, sat down in an armchair. Now that everything was out in the open she seemed almost less desirable. Or, rather, I had no great affection for the character that the present scenario would make me become.

'Do you remember that false dream you told me about at Ker Emma? A young man was chatting you up but refusing to admit his true feelings, and the sense of expectation created an incredible intensity.'

'I was asking you to give me a couple of weeks of courtship, not a whole year.'

'Come with me.'

I got up and opened the door.

'Where are we going?'

'Next door, on the same landing.'

Fanfan frowned and followed. We entered my studio. She saw the two-way mirror and gaped in astonishment. She examined all the details of my bedsit and was alarmed.

'This is where I've been living these last few weeks. I wanted to share your life without allowing humdrum existence to spoil the attraction between us. Now do you understand just how much I adore you?'

From her eyes I could see she had just grasped the secret behind my timely intervention on the night Jacques tried to rape her. Fanfan pushed me onto the bed:

'That's the past, this is the present...' she murmured.

'No, Fanfan,' I replied, without moving. 'I only showed you my flat so that you would realize how much I love you, to make you comprehend what it is that prevents me from becoming your husband or your lover. If you weren't the love of my life I'd have gone to bed with you ages ago.'

'Alexandre, Alexandre, let yourself go, come on...'

'No, Fanfan, I want our love to be like one long prelude, it must be perfect. I don't want to have to die to save it. I want to live the world's first imperishable passion, and the only way to achieve that is abstinence.'

'And what about me?' she challenged, bewildered.

'You get pleasure out of all this intensity as well, don't you?'

'You're mad.'

'Mad for the sake of love, the only madness worth having. Besides, would you love me if I wasn't?'

Fanfan tried to put an end to our debate by kissing me on the lips. I turned my head. Humiliated, she got up and left the room without another word.

The light came back on in her flat. She walked up to the two-way mirror and slowly removed her night gown. Then she caressed her breasts. She knew what a state I was in, and knowing she knew this made me even more excited. I walked up to the glass and so did she, as if she could feel my movements. I too took off my shirt. Our bodies touched. I removed my remaining clothes. We were pressed against each other, naked. I had a burning desire to smash the mirror, but knew that the obstacle formed by this cold surface was indispensable to the survival of our passion. Gradually, our overwrought desire led us to sublime but solitary ecstasy. Fanfan started to cry. God, she was so beautiful!

Resisting her now would really be torture.

The next morning I was woken up by the sound of my doorbell. I threw on my dressing gown and opened up.

'Well?' asked my father, not even bothering to say hello.

'Well what?'

'Fanfan!' And he shut the door behind him.

I didn't know what to say. I had mixed feelings. I knew that if I told this writer what had happened to me I would be selling off a part of my private life. But at the same time I was happy to see him so enthusiastic about my adventure. He was finally seeing me through the eyes of a proud father. I made some coffee as he besieged me with questions. His interest in my love life was directly proportionate to what he called his 'lack of imagination'. He had an extraordinary gift for reinventing reality, and absolutely no interest in working up a story from scratch. Dad got his kicks exclusively from direct reporting. I surmised that his new film-script was flagging.

In spite of our pact, I felt unable to tell him directly about what was still a cherished and idyllic romance. I therefore promised to give it to him in note form instead. This went against the grain, for what he wanted was freshly gathered news, but it was that or nothing.

'And what about you? How are things?' I attempted to change the subject.

'Well, I don't know how I feel. Something incredible's just happened.'

He told me that he had recently become the lover of a woman called Clara, the wife of a government minister. Now there was nothing unusual about a member of the cabinet being cuckolded, nor did I see anything out of the ordinary in my father making a new conquest. But I also learnt that this official had, in his youth, been the lover of Dad's mother – my grandmother – and become initiated into her erotic secrets. The minister had then passed this knowledge on to his wife. Which meant, therefore, that my father's mistress was, by virtue of her marriage, the guardian of the erotic skills acquired by my paternal grandmother.

'Do you know what I said to Clara when she told me all this?'

I felt horribly uncomfortable. 'No,' I replied.

'Do the same thing to me! And she did – exactly what my mother used to do to her husband!'

This charming revelation made me sick with anxiety.

My father had presented this story as an aesthete would. He failed to realize that what he had done with this woman had taken him into a region where the soul itself is in jeopardy. Once again, he had ceased to be either son or father and had become a Writer, a member of that abject profession whose vampire practitioners all too often go astray by asking more from life than it can possibly give them.

But my father was jubilant.

'Do you see?' he repeated, 'She did the same thing . . .'

This writerly madness filled me with dread, and once again I renewed my oath to love only one woman, and no other – that I would love her all my life and, to this end, that I would never respond to Fanfan's advances. I was convinced that abstinence was the only way to limit my desires to the same girl.

My father had seen Fanfan on the other side of the mirror, and was observing her, fascinated. She stretched and got up, dressed in her night gown.

'Ah,' he sighed, 'she's beautiful from every angle.'

Fanfan took up position in front of the two-way mirror and bade me good morning. Dad fairly jumped with surprise.

'But, she can see us!'

'No, she can't.'

'Then she knows you're there! What happened?'

'You can read about it later.'

Dad demanded an immediate explanation. I pushed him towards the door, urging him to leave before Fanfan came round. We'd be in real trouble if she found him there, I said. But my main concern was simply to be rid of him. He made me uneasy. I knew that no baseness was beyond him in his thirst for strong sensations. What he described as 'living with intensity' meant living uncomfortably, risking his neck every morning, forever defying the tax man, drinking ten cups of coffee a day and smoking enough to singe the beard of cancer.

'Are you coming to Verdelot this weekend?' he called from the landing. 'The whole gang'll be there.'

'No, no.' And I closed the door.

Verdelot: the word still struck fear into my heart. And even more so when combined with the presence of 'the gang' for the weekend. Just how many of my parents' mistresses and lovers did this ragbag contain? I didn't want to know, and nor did I want to be plunged back in amongst that brilliant but frightening menagerie. Just the thought of having to face their barely-contained jealousy, their extraordinary games of seduction and muted rivalries made me tired.

I preferred to head straight for Ker Emma that very evening. Tomorrow they would be holding the annual festivities in celebration of the sea wall.

ELEVEN

I ARRIVED AT KER EMMA AT ABOUT SEVEN IN THE
evening, local time. Monsieur Ti was still out in the
woods planting trees. It was his way of fighting against
old age. Fanfan was busy in Paris with Gabilan's film,
but would be joining us later for dinner.

I helped Maude prepare the meal. While washing a
lettuce, I asked her about her first husband, Fanfan's
grandfather. Maude lay down her potato peeler, and
went quiet. Seeing her silent like this, I hastened to
apologize for my curiosity.

'Oh, there's nothing to be sorry about, I love to talk
about Cho-Cho. That was what everyone called him.
He was ... a wonderful man. Yes, really wonderful.'

Maude returned to the business of helping a tuber out
of its jacket. The peelings were ultra-fine. Maude had
lived through the Occupation.

'By night Cho-Cho was a croupier in the casino at Deauville, and by day he was my lover.'

Again, she let the seconds drift by. Then she went on.

'I'm going to make a confession, something I have never told anyone else: Cho-Cho was a cheat. He knew how to throw the ball so that eight times out of ten it stopped on the number he had chosen. His skill was staggering. Yet he never used it for his personal advantage. He only cheated on behalf of people who had no idea he was doing it.'

'So what was the point?'

'To control chance. Every night, he decided who would win and who would lose. The vainer customers made some pretty heavy losses when he was at the wheel, I can tell you. He invented his own code of ethics and considered his job as a kind of mission. He had no interest in cheating just for its own sake. It was the same with money. What he liked was to throw the ball as an act of justice, to outface Providence.'

'When did he die?'

'Eight years ago.'

'What happened?'

'His hands had begun to shake. He couldn't control the ball any more ... It was all too much for his poor old heart. But I don't feel any jealousy towards the ball. It was because of Cho-Cho's death that I met Ti.'

I watched her dicing the potatoes and thought to myself that this Cho-Cho-the-croupier was probably just a pathological liar whose cardiac arrest was the result of too much hearty eating. Maude certainly had a heavy hand with the butter when she cooked. Naturally, I kept these thoughts to myself. Her version of events had the advantage of being beautiful; it deserved to be true.

'Men are so stupid with their mania for controlling everything.' She was looking at me intently as she said this.

I wondered if Fanfan had told her about my plan to postpone our first kiss until forever.

'Take my word for it, you have to put your trust in life!' she concluded, pinching me on the cheek.

So, now I knew. Fanfan had confided in her grand-mother. But Maude had the good taste not to go beyond allusion. As I gave the finishing touches to the meal, I thought with admiration of this eighty-seven-year-old woman who still had the gusto to slip her hand in Monsieur Ti's boxer shorts.

After dinner, Fanfan suggested that she and I go and take a midnight swim by the sea wall. The new warmth of early June justified her whim.

'I can't, I've got nothing to swim in,' was my cowardly reply.

'Nor have I. But whoever said you needed a swimming costume to take a midnight dip?'

'I'm tired. I'd rather go to bed.'

'All right, I'll go on my own.' She smiled. 'And without a costume.'

I ran up to my room on the second floor, turned the key twice in the lock and threw it out of the window to guard against any second thoughts. I could call for someone to open up the next morning.

Fanfan passed by below my window, whistling. Like a prisoner, I watched my siren head off towards the sea, then disappear into the pitch black night. I began to imagine her undressing on the sea wall. Our bodies brushing together in the water. My loins, my ever-present loins, informed me of their conviction that I had been a fool to throw away my key. I was obsessed with the image of her thighs moving apart on contact with mine. I went cold then hot with desire. My destiny lay with Fanfan. Maude was right. You have to put your trust in life.

I tried to open the lock using some nail tweezers. It wouldn't budge. I didn't dare break the door down, the noise would have disturbed or woken the customers of the hotel, and Maude would not have been very happy about the damage to her room. Then the idea came to me of acting like a hero of the silver screen. After all, my father was going to write a film based on our romance. I knotted my sheets together and climbed out through the window.

Fanfan was no longer on the sea wall.

'Fanfan! Fanfan?'

There was no answer, but in the half light I could just make her out. She was swimming. She was given away by the splashing noise of her arms. I undressed and plunged into the cold water.

'Fanfan.'

'. . .'

I put my hand on her shoulder. It was as cold as ice! For one terrible, horror-struck moment, I thought she had drowned, but then I realized I had touched a piece of wood smoothed down by the sea water into a shape which evoked a shoulder and a head resting on an arm.

I got out of the water. My ardour had cooled. I understood now that if Fanfan really had drowned that night I would not have lost her. Our strange relationship had accustomed me to having her live in my mind. I imagined it would be the same for her. The darkness of death would not be enough to keep us apart; unless of course I was weak enough to heed the call of my senses. For me, chastity was the only antidote to death.

The next day Fanfan had disappeared. Nobody at the Hôtel du Globe knew where she had gone. I spent the morning longing for her to come back. Though I knew she had vanished only to make herself more intensely desired, I still couldn't muster the strength to pretend I wasn't waiting for her.

The whole of Ker Emma was preparing for the anniversary of the completion of the sea wall built by Népomucène and Emma Sauvage. More than a thousand of their descendants, husbands and wives included, were busy on the beach. Some brought wood for the fires, others set up tables. Every kitchen in the town breathed out exquisite and enticing aromas. Children and adolescents raked the oak-lined avenues or mowed the lawns. Distant cousins engaged in animated conversation. Some lived in Minnesota or California, a few dozen had emigrated to other parts of France or to Europe, and a handful had put down roots in Africa. This year as every year, the branches of this one family came together to form a single tree. They were there to be counted, and so that their children, many of whom had grown up far from Ker Emma, would remember that they were members of a clan for which the word 'impossible' was meaningless. Had not Népomucène and Emma held back the thrust of the ocean?

Over lunch with Maude and Monsieur Ti I voiced my astonishment that none of these people were in any way ostentatious about their success. Modesty was the order of the day, and yet many had much to be immodest about.

'We hate competitiveness,' said Maude, by way of an answer.

'The children at the village school don't get marks for their work,' added Monsieur Ti. 'They are simply told whether or not they are making progress.'

'And what if they're not?'

Maude laughed. 'People treat them as if they were ill!'

Although there was not a single drop of Népomucène's blood running in my veins, I nevertheless felt I belonged to this tribe. Had I not surpassed myself in the continual repression of my instincts? I was as much a Sauvage as a Crusoé.

Every minute of the afternoon was marked by Fanfan's absence. I knew that she was capable of using whatever wiles were necessary to make me succumb. She would never give up. She was a true daughter of Ker Emma.

Night fell. On the beach, around the braziers, the people of Ker Emma struck up the Song of the Sea Wall, a comic hymn in a hundred couplets to the glory of Emma and Népomucène Sauvage. Among the dunes, amorous young relations discreetly 'related' to each other. It was almost a tradition here to spend this auspicious night sketching out one's future sex life in the company of distant cousins, and the verb 'to relate' had been coined and confirmed by successive generations specially for the occasion. The elders always pronounced it with a ring of nostalgia in their voices.

155

My anxiety grew. No one had seen Fanfan since she went for her midnight swim. Yet neither her parents, nor Maude nor Ti seemed unduly worried. They must have assumed that she was somewhere in the crowd. I searched in vain for a sight of her face around the fires.

Something told me that the piece of wood I had momentarily taken for her corpse was a harbinger of catastrophe. The more the people around me danced and laughed, the stronger my conviction grew that something terrible had happened to Fanfan out at sea. I imagined her being drowned. I was obsessed by the thought of that piece of wood floating in front of the sea wall. And I regretted the fact that I had never kissed her on the lips – not even once. Had she killed herself to prove that she could not live without me, or had there been an accident? The candles that lit up the tables suddenly seemed funereal, and the flower displays appeared as wreaths to me. It was as if this enormous family had come together for a wake. What a fool I'd been to imagine that our chastity would make it easier for me to bear her death. It only made it more painful. My distress was heightened by the nagging sense of incompleteness.

I was wandering along the shore when, at the end of the beach, near a fire surrounded by a circle of people, I saw a young woman performing a rather unorthodox flamenco. The onlookers were mainly on the youthful side and male. She was accompanied by a guitarist. I went closer. It was Fanfan, dressed like a Spaniard and made up like a whore. The men were ogling her plunging neckline. Her thighs were sheathed in black silk stockings held by a suspender belt whose lacy frills were glimpsed every time she twirled her dress. Fanfan stared at me frostily for a moment. The shadow of the flames flickering on her face made her look somehow demonic. She began to dance, swinging her hips and belly, her breathing getting heavier and heavier, as if she were simulating an orgasm. The men followed the undulations of her loins as they moved to the rhythm of the music. She smiled at them, brushed up against them, thrusting out her breasts and caressing their cheeks as she stepped tantalizingly backwards. Her hair was down. At one moment she was offering them her nape, at the next her throat. They all desired her, she seemed to desire each one. Our eyes met a second time. Her expression was stony. I realized now that this was no bluff. This evening, these men would be all over her body unless I gave in and kissed her. She was at the end of her tether and preferred to tarnish herself and drag me down into her suffering rather than bear my daily disdain. I was discovering to my cost just how far passion can drive a woman. She had planned the whole day with the aim of wearing down my patience, and thus destroying my capacity to withstand the present ordeal.

Fanfan leant towards me as she danced and murmured: 'Tonight they'll all be mine.'

A false smile appeared on her lips; then, on the last chord, she raised her hands in the air. The guitar was silent now. Fanfan let herself fall into the arms of some fair-haired youth. I hurried towards her.

'Fanfan, come with me!' I pulled her by the sleeve.

'Who on earth is he?' she exclaimed, contemptuously.

The blond tried to push me away. 'What do you want with her anyway?'

'Fanfan . . .'

ALEXANDRE JARDIN

'I've never seen him before.'

Without thinking twice I gave the young man a vigorous kick below the belt. He groaned and doubled up. I grabbed Fanfan by the arm and dragged her away from this hellish scene.

We came to a halt near the rocks, panting heavily in the shadows.

'All right,' I said. 'I'll be your lover. But once and only once in our lifetime. I don't want habit to come and ruin our passion. Do you understand? I want us to experience perfect love. Choose the date, right now. But there'll be only one night.'

'Tonight,' she said, sounding perfectly natural.

I was dumbfounded. How could I wriggle out of this one? I had made my offer to play for time and stop her flight into shame.

'It will be tonight,' she repeated with a smile.

'You realize, don't you, that this will be the one and only time?'

'Yes.'

'Okay then.'

Fanfan took my hand. The simple contact was overwhelming. At last I was going to possess the woman to whom my spirit had been in thrall for well over a year now. We set off towards the dunes. I tried to memorize the wafting fragrances of the sea, the light wind and the thousand sensations I was feeling: timidity, joy, disquiet, excitement. It was like shattering a mirror, scaling a summit. I felt fulfilled, whole. I knew this night of 'relating' would be the last and I was determined not to miss the slightest detail that would help me recall it in the future.

Fanfan lay down on the sand facing the stars and held out her hand. I warmed it for her, kissing and playing with her fingers. I kissed her palm and let my lips wander to the threshold of intimacy: the inside of her wrist. I was about to go further when she stopped me with a whispered 'No.'

'What is it?'

'Tonight, you shall have only my hand.'

'What are you talking about?' I exclaimed, shocked.

'If I let you have all of me tonight then you'd be capable of ensuring that there were no other occasions. I want to frustrate you, to have you dying, burning to sleep with me again. All you can have this evening is my hand and, perhaps, up to my elbow.'

'Fanfan, you're breaking our agreement.'

'Well you imposed it on me. Don't tell me you'd really like it if I gave myself up to you the very first time you actually condescended to make me an offer! Now it's your turn to suffer what I've endured for so long. You'll have to make do with what I give you,' she concluded, stretching her hand towards me.

I drew back instinctively, recoiling from the shackles she was hoping to bind me with.

'No,' I shouted. 'It's all on one night or nothing!' I was back on my feet.

Fanfan panicked. She leapt up and grabbed hold of my trousers. Then, as if issuing a challenge, she said, 'All right, tonight you shall have everything.'

She spoke as if she were totally confident of her erotic power. Her assurance both worried and fascinated me.

We made love under the stars, going beyond modesty, in a communion of renewed trust and tenderness,

159

ALEXANDRE JARDIN

of total abandon and caring restraint. Fanfan was a source of surprises that flowed freely until dawn.

That was when she asked me, 'Do you want to do it again?'

'If the pleasures of these last hours had been less sublime, then perhaps I would be tempted to yield to your pressure a second time. But why should we take the risk of tarnishing our memory of this perfect night?'

Fanfan shut her eyes.

TWELVE

I HAD GIVEN IT CAREFUL THOUGHT. ALL THAT remained for me was to die. Naturally, I intended to go on enjoying life, but for our passion to remain at its peak I had to be dead for Fanfan.

Our night of love meant we could never go back to the enchantments of our first beginnings; my whole being rebelled against the idea that our violent attraction for each other would suffer gradual attrition. I wanted us to live the kind of love story that could inspire a great work of fiction. Shakespeare and Musset had taught me that only death can make passion transcendent. It was therefore necessary to go over to the other side.

I opted for drowning in the ocean, which had the advantage of giving credibility to the disappearance of my corpse. All I had to do was set out to sea in a dinghy

161

without a life jacket but with witnesses. A mile or so from the coast, I would capsize and then abandon the boat and swim back to land. All I needed was to have some dry clothes ready for me near Monsieur Ti's lighthouse or somewhere else and I could then sneak back to Paris. I could just imagine what they'd say when they found the boat: 'It can happen so easily, a knock on the head from the boom and ... yup, it must have knocked him unconscious ... If only he'd been a bit more sensible and taken a life jacket. Poor kid, to think he was only twenty, etc.'

The fact that Fanfan and I had so few mutual acquaintances would make the illusion of my death that much easier to sustain. I could trust Gabilan with the secret, but my mother would be certain to reject such a 'cruel trick'. Still, I could always remind her of how she treated her men – not much better. As for Dad, I was sure my idea would satisfy his requirements as a script-writer. Gabilan would find my initiative amusing. He loved unusual deeds.

Maude and Monsieur Ti were a more difficult case. They would be a great loss to me, these grandparents whose thoughts enriched me and whose way of living embodied my ideal of happiness, but after all this it would be impossible to go on seeing them. If I came back to Ker Emma, Fanfan would be bound to find out sooner or later. With a heavy heart, then, I resolved to become dead for them as well.

My decision was made, but that didn't shield me from a host of upsetting questions. Had I begun to go mad? What right did I have to inflict such suffering on Fanfan? Surely, my plan was pure egotism? And what about love in all this? What was I running away from when I chose death? All these nagging doubts were beginning to make me uncomfortable. I banished them and told myself that there could be nothing wrong in making myself undergo what is, after all, the fate of every self-respecting romantic hero.

This absorbing inner dialogue took place in my flat. I was about to drink some apple juice when Fanfan came home. I put down my glass.

She walked up to the two-way mirror and said, 'If you're there, knock on the glass. I need to speak to you. It's important.'

I gave two knocks, and this is what she said: 'My love, today I'm going away to Italy, to Rome. The shoot will take five days, and I'll be back here at ten-thirty on Friday evening. I'll wait for you in this flat for a quarter of an hour. If you don't come and kiss me and ask for my hand in marriage you'll never see me again. Do you hear? Never again.'

She picked up her overnight bag and turned to face me: '*Ciao, bambino.*'

And with that she was gone.

Her ultimatum forced me to kill myself. There was no alternative. I had no right to let her ride roughshod over our passion.

I was off to Ker Emma.

On the train, I went over all the details that needed to be dealt with to make my demise fully convincing to Fanfan. For one thing, in the script my father was writing the young man would have to die at the end too. If he didn't perish, his survival might make Fanfan doubt the reality of my own death when she saw the film. I would also ask my father to tell her that there would be no religious service, and that since my body could not be found there could be no tomb either. That way my mother would be spared having to shed fake tears at a bogus funeral. Besides, I imagined it would be far too complicated to find a suitable accomplice among the priesthood. The absence of a grave would make it more difficult for Fanfan to mourn and for my father to bring out his film. And that was my aim. I wanted her to keep me alive in her heart forever. Embalmed love is immune to change.

As I walked through Ker Emma a strange sensation came over me. In a few hours, I would be dead for this village. The people who crossed my path were seeing a young man living out his last moments on earth.

I walked into the Hôtel du Globe, overcome with emotion. It seemed to me as if it were not myself but Monsieur Ti and Maude who were about to expire. I stopped in the foyer. There was no one there. I wiped my eyes, which had begun to shine. My sadness grew as the realization sank in that I would never set foot in this place again. Now, for the first time, I noticed the bouquets decorating the entrance. Flowers everywhere. I felt as though I had just woken up. The sound of chinking glass drew me to the bar. Ti stood with his back to me behind the counter, arranging his bottles of spirits for unlikely patrons. It was still the low season. He turned round. A tear made its way slowly down my cheek. Monsieur Ti noticed it.

'Hello, Alexandre,' he said.

I bowed my head. I didn't have the courage to leave

him for good. He watched me in silence, and filled two small glasses with an eau-de-vie he called his 'elixir'.

I leant on the zinc counter, facing him, my nose over my glass. There was a long silence which he refused to break. Ti knew that the tension would force me to speak my mind.

I told him everything that had happened since the night I met Fanfan. His insistent silence forced me to confess everything. When I came to the end he poured me another elixir.

'So, that's why I'm here. To pass myself off as drowned.'

Monsieur Ti let another minute pass before declaring, 'You know, one of these days you'll have to leave your adolescence behind you.'

'Adolescence?' The word surprised me.

'You're just a greenhorn, a young'un wet behind the ears. You don't understand a thing, do you? How much longer are you going to act like a kid with a crush? Alexandre, it's time you became a man. I know that adolescence is the scourge of the century, that we're all chronic teenagers. You're not the only one. There are millions of you, desperate to 'stay young', chickening out of commitment, stuck in the rut of your youth, aping the ways of pubescent kids, preferring passion to love. Love? You're incapable of it. And I'm talking about real love here, love that gives, not virgin love. I suppose you'll tell me that "it has its satisfactions". Well, if you swallow all that toxic nonsense your soul will be polluted. I believe in pure love. Yes, and I maintain that that's what we're here for. Not for passion. This is something I learnt recently, in Maude's arms, when I was eighty-four. "Perpetual passion" is an adolescent notion. The idea of commitment scares you shitless! Stop trying to escape your humanity with all those idiotic stratagems of yours. For God's sake, have the courage to be a man! Keeping alive your childhood self doesn't mean you have to stay a child. You're like those people who are always zapping from one channel to another so they see only the most exciting bits. It's pure idiocy. Stories are made to develop. Believe me, unending passion is an illusion, a seductive illusion. If you put too much salt in your cooking you kill its subtlest flavours. When you play music too loud you miss some of the notes. Great lovers are musical lovers, gourmets of feeling – not guzzlers of chilli peppers. Passion and love are two very different things. Your contempt for couples is childish, and you're as puerile as your parents. Oh yes, by perpetuating the preamble to love you are avoiding all the risks, keeping the difficulties at arm's length. But difficulties are also a part of life and it's a spineless existence that doesn't face up to them. You can't love without running the risk of failure. That's the price you have to pay. And believe me, living with another human being is about the only adventure we have left. Communism, the moon, America, all that's finished now. If you miss out on marriage you'll have missed out on the most important experience of our times. Forgive me if I get so worked up about this, but when I see you playing the imbecile I'm reminded of my own mistakes. I was like you once, interested only in passion. But then, thank God, I met Maude. We were old, but at least we would enjoy a few years of love together. And then what about Fanfan, for Christ's

166

sake? You should re-read *Le Petit Prince*! We have a responsibility towards those we love. You have no right to destroy her hopes. You've been a real bastard with her. To toy with a woman's heart is sacrilege. Women are too beautiful for that! Believe me, people who shirk commitment are extras, not actors. They're a disgrace to the species. It is a privilege to be human and we must show ourselves worthy of it. So for God's sake marry Fanfan and get yourself a proper job, and stop trying to fill your empty life with passion. Tell me, what have you got to show for your talent? You waste your energy in twisted games, eat up your father's income and break Fanfan's heart. Now just you remember this: the only thing on this earth that is of any importance is making a woman happy. The rest is vanity. I utterly forbid you to pass yourself off as dead. It's unworthy of you. Live your life, don't run away into some sham death. And don't forget, the greatest adventure of our age is marriage. Don't wait until you're as old as I am to understand.'

I was dazed, stunned. Ti drank an elixir then, in a voice thick with emotion:

'I'm telling you this because . . .'

I put my hand on his, stood up, and left the hotel.

At ten-thirty on Friday evening, Fanfan entered her room, lay on her bed without so much as a glance at the mirror, and closed her eyes. I was standing behind the glass.

I had been waiting for this moment to make my mind up. By now I really didn't know what to think, so I stopped reasoning and let my instinct guide me.

I pressed close to the mirror then, suddenly, smashed

it with a stool. Our two flats were one. Fanfan didn't move. I went in – to our home – put my face close to hers and kissed her on the lips.

My princess opened her eyes.

'Will you marry me?' I murmured.

'Yes,' answered Fanfan.

The next morning I went round to my father's house. He opened the door and kissed me on the cheeks. For the first time in my life, I realized that we were the same height. God, he really did look like me. Seeing us in the hall mirror you'd think we were twin brothers.

He made me a coffee and said he was planning to give my mother a stuffed bison for her birthday.

'Do you think she'd like that?'

'Dad, I'm going to write the story of my romance with Fanfan. Your film will be an adaptation of the novel.'

He went quiet, stared at me, then sobbed like a child.

'My son, at last, my son!' His eyes were drowned in tears.

'Yes, my dear old Dad, and it's about time you became a father.'

'I know, I know . . .'

Our wedding was held in the church at Verdelot. This was a departure from the tradition whereby one's great passion is celebrated on the woman's territory, but I wanted our ceremony to take place on the battleground where my parents continued to engage in amorous combat.

With tears in my eyes I entered the packed church, my mother at my side. Adieu adolescence, adieu

Alexandre the child. She led me to the altar, past all her lovers. For the first time, I looked on these grown-up children as my fathers. My mother left me as we reached the choir stalls and returned to her seat, beside my father, whose name I bear. Behind him sat his mistress. They were all there, their childhood written in their faces. I could feel that they were moved and yet terrified. I was their son, and already a man. They couldn't believe that the child born of their amours was an adult.

Monsieur Ti and Maude had been unable to make the trip. They were too old to leave Ker Emma. They were represented by Hermantrude. Next to her sat Titanic, eyeing her with undisguised lust. Hermantrude was in seventh heaven. Mado was there too, praying.

I heard the sound of murmuring behind me, then silence. Footsteps echoed through the nave. I turned and saw Fanfan dressed in white, on her father's arm. Why did I cry? She walked slowly forward, her shoulders bare, her veil like a halo. The present was at one with eternity. Approaching me, I saw the old woman she would be one day. I saw her future wrinkles and they made her almost more beautiful. My father's eyes met mine. He smiled. He knew what I had lived through.

Now the priest made his entrance. This sensualist and mystic was a friend. He spoke of love and only love, alluding to the written oaths Fanfan and I had exchanged during the religious preparation for our marriage – intimate and unabashed vows of undying fidelity. And then, all of a sudden, he was reading these same vows out loud. The priest was the only person who knew of them, and we certainly hadn't authorized him to divulge their contents. Fanfan blushed deeply and squeezed my hand to keep up her strength. That the priest had taken this cavalier initiative made my head spin with happiness. As a man familiar with my strange family he knew exactly what resonance these bold professions would have when declaimed like this in the church.

I looked across at the first pews. My mother and my father were sobbing. We were all seekers in the same quest. Now it was my turn to understand them. I was filled with a deep joy.

'The swine,' murmured Fanfan, unaware of my joy.

The priest blessed the rings and came close to us.

'Fanfan, do you take Alexandre as your husband?'

'Yes.' Her reply was proud and triumphant.

'Alexandre, do you take Fanfan for your wife, for better or for worse?'

'Yes!' I cried, lifting her in my arms.

We had many children and I became a writer and, contrary to all expectations, we were very happy.